The World is About to Laugh Like it Has Never Laughed Before

Laughter has no language, knows no boundaries,
does not discriminate between caste, creed and colour.
It is a powerful emotion and has all the ingredients for
uniting the entire world.

Mission: World Peace Through Laughter

This book is dedicated to my mother Raj Karni Kataria
and my only wife Madhuri

aha ha ho ha ho ha ho ha ha
ha ha ho ha ho ha ho ha ha
ho ha ha ha ho ha ho ha ho ha
o ho ha ha ho ha ho ha ho
ha ho ho

L a u g h
For No Reason

DR. MADAN KATARIA
Founder President
Laughter Club International

First Edition : 1999

Second Edition: 2002

Published by:
MADHURI INTERNATIONAL
A-1, Denzil, 3rd Cross Road,
Lokhandwala Complex,
Andheri (W), Mumbai - 400 053.
Tel: 91-22 - 2631 6426 Fax: 91-22 - 2632 0945
E-mail: laugh@laughteryoga.org or drkataria@hotmail.com
Website: www.laughteryoga.org

ISBN 81-87529-01-6

Photos by Jean-Claude < jc.jaffre@online.fr >

QUANTITY SALES

This book is available at a special discount when purchased in bulk by corporations, organisations or groups. Special imprints, messages and excerpts can be produced to meet your needs.

WEBSITE ORDERS
You can also buy this book on our website : www.laughteryoga.org

The publishers are looking for experts to translate this book into all languages all over the world. Those interested may send their details to **Madhuri International** *at the address given above.*

This book gives non-specific, general advice and should not be relied on as a substitute for proper medical consultation. The author and publisher cannot accept responsibility for illness arising out of the failure to seek medical advice from a doctor.

CONTENTS

Before You Begin to Laugh With Us

The idea of starting a Laughter Club came to me as a flash when I was writing an article, "Laughter - the Best Medicine", for a health magazine I used to edit. It was on the 13th of March 1995, when the first Laughter Club was started in a public park of Mumbai (Bombay), India, with just five people. Today, after eight years, it has grown into a worldwide laughter movement. This small seed has bloomed into a big 'Laughing Family' of more than 2500 clubs all over the world in countries like India, USA, UK, Canada, Australia, Germany, France, Italy, Sweden, Norway, Denmark, Finland, Ireland, Hungary, Switzerland, Singapore, Malaysia, Vietnam and Dubai. The amount of interest shown by people around the world leaves me with little doubt that this laughter movement is a kind of Divine Wisdom and I am glad that it has been manifested through me.

I must confess that I am not a person with an extraordinary sense of humour, nor am I a comedian or a great joke teller. I am not a yoga expert and neither am I very well versed in the *Vedas, Upanishads* or *Gita*. I am only a physician who comes from a large agricultural family, from a small village with a population of not more than five hundred. I lived my childhood with rustic, innocent and hard-working people. My experience with villagers taught me that laughter can come to you easily and in abundance if you have a childlike heart full of love and innocence. People in big cities try to block their laughter for the sake of looking good and they deny themselves the manifold benefits of that wonderful gift from God, the capacity to laugh.

This book seeks to inform all those who would like to know what the concept of a Laughter Club is, how it started and what it seeks to achieve. What are its programmes and procedures, aims and objects, hopes and aspirations?

A number of people have said kind things about me. While I am very grateful to them I must mention that it has, all along, been a combined effort of Laughter Club members from all over the world. It will not be incorrect to say that each member of every Laughter Club has contributed, in one way or the other, to the growth of Laughter Clubs. My role has been only that of the facilitator.

When we started the Laughter Clubs, it was meant to combine laughter-exercises based on yogic breathing and stretching techniques to make the benefits of laughter accessible, freely and free of cost to one and all. Since 1997, we found a new meaning of laughter. This is that laughter is not only amusement and entertainment, neither is it all giggling and chuckling. Laughter has to come right from within, from one's soul. One can experience laughter from the soul only when the heart is pure, full of love, kindness and compassion. Laughter becomes more meaningful when it is intended not only to make oneself happy, but also to make others happy. This is what is known in Laughter Clubs, as the "Spirit of Laughter".

Through this beautiful platform of Laughter Clubs, we all will try to bring about attitudinal changes, so that we can live in peace and harmony. It will not be very long before the slogan, "World Peace Through Laughter" becomes a reality. It is my firm belief that we have already started out on the journey towards a "Unified World", where every human being in the world belongs to a single religion - that of LAUGHTER.

DR. MADAN KATARIA
A-1, Denzil, 3rd Cross Road, Lokhandwala Complex,
Andheri (W), Mumbai - 400 053. INDIA Tel: 91-22 - 2631 6426
Fax: 91-22 - 2632 0945 E-mail: laugh@laughteryoga.org
Website: www.laughteryoga.org

ACKNOWLEDGMENTS

From just five persons on 13th of March, 1995, to more than 2500 Laughter Clubs all over the world and hundreds of articles in prestigious publications worldwide, to the laughter story appearing on many television networks and thousands of request letters from all over the world for new Laughter Clubs, all these indicate that such clubs are indeed no laughing matter. This has certainly not been achieved by me alone. I am not that capable. I would like to salute the Divine Force which has chosen to manifest itself through me. Though I did generate the concept of Laughter Clubs, the laughter movement has reached its current size and stature due to the untiring efforts of the following people, to whom I would like to extend my love and gratitude.

First and foremost, my loving wife Madhuri, who has dedicated her life to the cause. Another Laughologist who needs to be applauded is P.T. Hinduja, who understood the power behind laughter and has worked tirelessly towards this cause, even at the age of 75. I can't forget the contribution of late J.K. Kapur, who was the Senior Vice President of the Laughter Club International and young, dynamic Mohit Kapoor from Worli Laughter Club, and B.P. Hirani from Jogger's Park Laughter Club helped to make my dream come true i.e the formation of the Laughter Club International as well as the organisation of two big events, World Laughter Day and the Laughter Convention which shook the whole world with laughter.

I would like to thank the anchor persons of a large number of Laughter Clubs who have put in tremendous efforts to spread this message all over the world. Among them are Kamini Bathija (Joggers Park, Bandra),

G.P.Shethia, Manubhai Turakhia, Devendra Jaawre (Nasik), L.N.Daga (Kolkata), S.K.Shrivastava (Nagpur), Mahendrabhai Shah (Ahmedabad), Shirin Punjwani (Hydrabad), Bhanu Bhandari (Ahmednagar), B.K. Satyanarayan (Bangalore), the late S.R. Agarwal (Raipur), Arvind Shah (Kolhapur), P.N Desai (Bhopal), Prof R.P.Gupta (Baroda) and many others.

My gratitude goes to Steve Wilson, a psychologist and America's popular joyologist, who invited me to United States in 1999 to start the laughter movement for the first time outside India. My special thanks to Arya Patharia (California), Vishwa Prakash (New York/Hong Kong). Thank you dear Francisca Munk (Norway), Maud Skoog Brandin, Charlotte Schanner, Lena Ulfsdotter Högnelid and Sofia (Sweden), Jan Thygesen Poulsen (Denmark), Robert W.L.Butt (Germany), Eva Bischofberger (Switzerland), Roberta Fidora and Isis (Italy), Daniel Kiefer (France), Shirley Hicks and Susan Welch (Australia), Thomas Chee Kin and Zareen Bana (Singapore), Ram (Dubai), Mahes Karuppiah (Malaysia), Paul Maguire and Julie Whitehead (London), Ferenc Domjan (Hungary) and Valgerdur Snaeland Jonsdottir (Iceland), Michel Abitbol and Dave & Jan MacQuarrie (Canada). Essi Tolonen (Finland), Marc De Wilde (Belgium) and Mary Mitchell (Ireland). All these laughter leaders have played a significant role in spreading the message of love and laughter globally.

CHAPTER - 1

Yogic Laughter - A BREAKTHROUGH!

Over the past two decades, extensive research has been conducted all over the world and it has been proved that laughter has a positive impact on various systems of the body. Laughter helps to remove the negative effects of STRESS, which is the number one killer today. More than 70% of illnesses like high blood pressure, heart disease, anxiety, depression, frequent coughs and colds, peptic ulcers, insomnia, allergies, asthma, menstrual difficulties, tension headaches, stomach upsets and even cancer, have some relations to stress. It has also been proved beyond a shadow of doubt that laughter helps to boost the IMMUNE SYSTEM, which is the master key for maintaining good health.

PEOPLE HAVE FORGOTTEN HOW TO LAUGH: Scientists are convinced that laughter has both preventive and therapeutic value. But these days, where is laughter? It seems as if people have forgotten how to laugh. According to a study done by Dr. Micheal Titze, a German Psychologist, "In the 1950's people used to laugh 18 minutes a day, but today we laugh not more than 6 minutes per day, despite the huge rises in the standard of living." Children can laugh up to 300-400 times in a day, but when we grow into adults this frequency comes down to just 15 times a day. Due to excessive seriousness, our sense of humor is also getting sick. The things at which we used to laugh heartily 30 years ago no longer stimulate even the faintest smile.

SENSE OF HUMOUR IS UNCOMMON AND UNCERTAIN: Today we can't depend on the sense of humour to create laughter, since humour is a very mental and intelligent phenomenon. Everyone does not have a sense of humour. Everyone cannot tell jokes or understand them fully. It is true that one must have a sense of humour to be able to laugh, but this is also true that very few people have a sense of humour. That means that the majority of people are not able to laugh, because of a lack of the sense of humour.

HOW TO LAUGH AND WHO WILL MAKE YOU LAUGH: Jokes can't make you laugh every day and a sense of humour is not everyone's cup of tea. The million-dollar question is how to laugh and who will make you laugh? Here is a BREAKTHROUGH! For the first time Dr. Madan Kataria, a Mumbai (India) - based physician has developed a new technique: free group laughter based on yoga (*Hasya Yoga*). Anyone can participate in group laughter, every day for 15-20 minutes, without resorting to jokes. Each laughter session starts with deep breathing and a Ho-Ho, Ha-Ha exercise, followed by a variety of stimulated laughter techniques like hearty laughter, silent laughter, medium laughter, lion laughter, swinging laughter, one meter laughter, cocktail laughter, gradient laughter and many others.

IT IS NOT DIFFICULT TO LAUGH WITHOUT A REASON: Self-induced, stimulated laughter can easily be converted into real laughter when you do it in a group. Laughter is infectious, laughter is contagious and it spreads when you laugh in company and have good eye contact. We have all laughed without a reason when we were children. Children can laugh for no reason

The historical first Laughter Club at Lokhandwala Complex, Mumbai, India.

because they have very few inhibitions. The very essence of laughing without a reason lies in developing your child-like spirit and playful attitude. If you can do that, laughter will come to you with great ease.

DEVELOPING A SENSE OF HUMOUR THROUGH LAUGHTER: If a sense of humour leads to laughter, the reverse is also true. When you try to laugh in a group for NO REASON, your inhibitions are broken and a sense of humour flows. This is exactly the BREAKTHROUGH we have achieved in our Laughter Clubs. We are finding our sense of humour through laughter.

A sense of humour is the capacity of an individual to perceive, relate and experience a given situation in a more funny and humorous way. A sense of humour is nothing that one is born with, but it is a skill which can be acquired with practice. One thing that God has given everyone of us is a tremendous potential to laugh. As you can see, a child can laugh up to 300-400 times a day. The child does not laugh because it has a sense of humour, but because it is in the nature of the child to be joyful. As the child starts growing he is exposed to more and more information and his laughter starts getting lost under layers of seriousness, self-control, responsibility, fear and insecurity. As a result, an ordinary situation at which the child used to be amazed and amused, does not trigger any good feeling any more.

To develop a sense of humour, one needs to remove the layers of inhibition and the mental blocks which have been created by oneself, one's parents and society. Once these barriers are removed, the infinite potential to laugh will unfold automatically and a sense of humour will start flowing. Teaching a person who has a lot of inhibitions to develop a sense of humour is like flushing a drain which is blocked with rubble. Once you remove the blockade, water will start flowing. This is exactly what has happened in Laughter Clubs. It is for this reason that we are successful in making thousands of people laugh in a country like India, where people hardly ever laugh or smile. The same people who never used to smile have started cracking jokes and enjoying jokes in a better way than ever before. They have started being playful and creative. Here, nobody was first trained to have a sense of humour and then laughed. We all laughed and laughed for no reason and without applying much logic. Therefore, it is not always the sense of humour that leads to laughter, but laughter can also help you to develop a sense of humour. Humour and laughter make one unity, each flows into the other.

By volunteering to laugh in a group we are preparing the grounds for a sense of humour to flow. Therefore, if you and I don't have a sense of humour don't worry: you have to laugh yourself silly and your sense of humour will start flowing. Laughter Clubs are the ideal platforms to laugh your way to silliness, because there is no fear of ridicule by anyone.

PHILOSOPHY OF 'FAKE IT UNTIL YOU MAKE IT': There is sufficient data available from medical research to show that even if you pretend to laugh or act happy your body produces happiness chemicals. According to the principles of Neuro Linguistic Programming (NLP) whether you laugh spontaneously at a joke or a situation, or whether you stimulate laughter (with willingness), it is still a form of exercise. Our bodies do not know

Laughter Club members are from every age group - school children, college students, housewives, doctors, engineers and elderly people.

the difference between thinking about doing something and actually doing it. Therefore, whatever may be the source of laughter it leads to the same set of physiological changes occurring in our bodies. Many actors and actresses all over the world have experienced the effect of faking emotions. Many times they felt sick after acting out sadness. This clearly indicates that if acting sadness can make you sick, ACTING HAPPINESS can make you HEALTHY. The idea of Laughter Clubs is based on this philosophy of acting happiness. Another theory is called MOTION CREATES EMOTIONS. If you put your body into an act of happiness, your mind will follow.

WILLINGNESS FACTOR: The most important factor in a Laughter Club is your WILLINGNESS TO LAUGH. Though the members of Laughter Clubs laugh out voluntarily, it is with full commitment and willingness. If you are not willing to laugh, nobody in this world can make you laugh. On the other hand, if you are willing to laugh and give yourself permission to laugh nobody can stop you from laughing. You don't even need any reason to laugh.

LAUGHTER YOGA ACTIVATES LAUGH MUSCLES: Yogic laughter exercise is not a SUBSTITUTE for the spontaneous laughter which we get throughout the day. As a matter of fact it helps to increase our capacity to laugh during the day. According to another research study, if you stretch your laugh muscles on a regular basis it will make them respond more spontaneously whenever there is something amusing. Group laughter exercises help members to reduce their inhibitions which enables them to laugh more often.

LAUGHTER AND ITS YOGA CONNECTION: A typical laughter session is a blend of yogic deep breathing, stretching, stimulated laughter exercises and cultivating child-like playfulness. The whole concept of group laughter exercises is based on yoga, which produces a unique physiological balance in our bodies, by connecting body, mind and spirit. Stimulated laughter exercises have been combined with DEEP BREATHING which is an important part of yoga. Deep breathing helps to stimulate the calming branch of our nervous system (Parasympathetic system) by rhythmic movement of the diaphragm and abdominal muscles. Deep breathing helps to increase the net supply of oxygen, which is the most important component of our metabolism. According to principles of yoga, laughter gives a constant massage to the digestive tract and also improves blood supply to all the internal organs. Laughter stimulates blood circulation which helps to transport nutrients all over the body and it also strengthens our respiratory apparatus which supplies oxygen to the body.

UNFOLDING INFINITE POTENTIAL THROUGH LAUGHTER: The human brain has a left and a right hemisphere. The left side of the brain is analytical, logical, calculative and concerned with learning skills. The capacity of the left side is LIMITED. You can't learn beyond a certain limit. The right side of the brain is concerned with intuition, imagination, inventions, music, art, creativity, meditation and healing. The power of the right side of the brain is UNLIMITED. One of the easiest ways to stimulate the right side of the brain is by playfulness. By being playful one can become more creative and imaginative. It will unfold the unlimited potential of our beings, but the problem with most of us is that we can't be playful all the time or with everybody. A Laughter Club is an ideal platform which gives an opportunity to be playful in a group, without a feeling of embarrassment.

ADDING NEW DIMENSIONS TO LAUGHTER: Most people think that laughter is only for amusement and entertainment, so that one can feel relaxed. Laughter is not merely a physical phenomenon. It does not make any sense if a Laughter Club member laughs a lot at the Laughter Club in the morning and keep screaming and shouting at his wife the whole day at home. Therefore, one should not laugh only for oneself. It is the responsibility of every Laughter Club member to make others also happy. Laughter should be reflected in one's behaviour and attitudes towards others. The members of Laughter Clubs do not only laugh, but they also practice ways and means of sensible living.

Through group discussions we identify all the negative factors which stop us from laughing. For example: anger, fear, guilt and jealousy are some of the negative emotions which produce negative feelings in us. In a group effort we try to cultivate positive emotions like love, appreciation, kindness, forgiveness and joy. The motto of Laughter Club members is not only to make themselves happy, but also to make others happy. This is known as the SPIRIT OF LAUGHTER. The inner spirit of laughter can be cultivated easily in a group effort. As a group the members of Laughter Clubs inspire and motivate each other. We know so many good things in life, but we don't get motivation to practise them, but if we do it in a group it happens in a much easier way.

LIBERATING YOUR LAUGHTER FROM REASON: Normally, people look for some reason to laugh, but these days, because of the stress and strain of modern living, there are very few things which make us laugh, while there are hundreds of things that can make us frown, howl and cry. Like laughter, happiness has also become conditional. Our happiness depends upon so many pre-conditions. Our happiness and laughter has become dependent on material success and personal achievements. Laughter is an expression of happiness. If we can learn to laugh unconditionally our

Leading Gynaecologists of Mumbai city participating in a laughter session.

happiness too will become unconditional. Therefore, liberate your laughter and happiness from reason by joining a Laughter Club; it will give you joy forever.

WISDOM BECOMES MANIFEST IN A GROUP: We have a wealth of eastern and western wisdom which, if practised, can help us to lead a happy and blissful life. One may acquire knowledge about swimming after reading a number of books, but all remains good for nothing if one does not get into the water and start to swim. This is the problem with most of us, that our knowledge about so many good things in life is not manifested because of lack of motivation. We know the theory but we do not put it into practice. The success of Laughter Clubs is attributed to a group effort. We know so many good things in life, but we don't get motivation to practise them. If we do it in a group though, it happens in a much easier way. Nobody would have thought one could laugh without jokes. It happened only when we all ventured into trying laughter as a group effort. In a group the motivation levels are very high. You don't have to do it, it just happens. You will do it because others are doing it.

If we can laugh together, we can also practise ways and means of sensible living together.

LAUGHTER SUITS ALL AND IS USER FRIENDLY: Laughter exercise is short and sweet and can be conveniently added to your existing fitness programmes. It will be a value addition at yoga groups, tai-chi groups, aerobic centres, meditation centres, health clubs, sports and fun activities. Already laughter yoga has been included in the curriculum of yoga sessions all over the world. Thousands of yoga practitioners have added 5-10 minutes of unconditional laughter at the end of their yoga sessions. You may not have to take special time out to laugh. The only requirement is that it should be practised in a group and on a daily basis if possible. Most important is that it does not depend upon external factors but on your own internal resources. Whenever, wherever the group decides to, they can laugh and gain the benefits. If you are a working person, group laughter will give you instant relaxation and help you to increase well being, so that you can work hard throughout the day. If you are the kind of person who needs to socialise and increase social contacts and become a part of a support group, it has a social medicine in it. This kind of format is ideally suited for retired people and the elderly. If you are a person with intelligent introspection and a spiritual inclination it has a lot of philosophy in it. You can learn the art of living through laughter. In a nutshell, the concept of Laughter Clubs has something for everyone to learn and get benefits from.

WORLD PEACE: THE MANTRA FOR THE NEW MILLENNIUM: There is war in the world because we are at war within ourselves. If we can bring peace inside us there will be peace outside. If we can bring peace inside us by practising yogic laughter and following ways and means of sensible living and these Laughter Clubs multiply all over the world, there will be everlasting peace on this planet.

CHAPTER - 2

Why Do We Need to Laugh More Today?

Today, life is very stressful and stress-related diseases are on the rise. More than 70% of illnesses have some relation to stress. High blood pressure, heart disease, anxiety, depression, frequent coughs and colds, nervous breakdowns, peptic ulcers, insomnia, allergies, asthma, irritable bowel syndrome, colitis, menstrual difficulties, migraine and even cancer have some relation to stress. To escape stress, people turn to alcohol, smoking and drugs. If you suffer from any of the following symptoms, you are probably heading for any of the above diseases or a combination of them:

❖ Nagging ache at the base of the neck
❖ Frequent headaches with tender temples
❖ Lethargy and constant fatigue
❖ Frequent coughs and colds
❖ Stomach knots
❖ Nausea and indigestion
❖ Irritable bowels or constipation

* Muscle tension with backache and neckache
* Altered sleep patterns e.g. difficulty in going to sleep, early waking.
* Breathlessness, bouts of dizziness, light-headedness
* Increase/decrease in eating
* Increased smoking or drinking
* Loss of sexual drive
* Frequent mood swings
* Feeling of isolation
* Lack of self-worth
* Frequent memory lapses
* Poor decision-making abilities
* Irritability and aggression
* Difficulty in concentration and alloting priorities
* Suicidal tendency

All of us get some of the above symptoms off and on in this fast paced life, but, if the symptoms recur and persist for a long time, you need to unwind and become a member of a Laughter Club. People try a number of relaxation techniques like exercise, massage, yoga, meditation and going for holidays, picnics and outings. All these methods are time consuming and expensive. One needs concentration and will power to stick to these methods. Most exercise programmes are abandoned due to boredom and lack of motivation. Yogic laughter (*Hasya Yoga*) in a group is one of the easiest and most economical de-stressing measures. Not only do we laugh in a group, but we also practice and implement ways and means of sensible living. Due to the group effort, motivation levels are high and there is no boredom, it being a short and sweet exercise.

All the perils of modern living have resulted from competition. While healthy competition is necessary for growth and development, it seems that today competition is unlimited. It makes us feel like losers even if we are winners. It puts a person at the top in stress for fear of losing his position. If someone overtakes you, it brings a sense of shame and depression and negative feelings of inferiority and jealousy. Due to this, people can't celebrate their small achievements and this leads to dissatisfaction and frustration, which in turn lead to drug addiction, alcoholism, gambling, violence and corruption. In a collective effort to understand life in a better way and live more joyfully we have created the platform of Laughter Clubs, where like-minded people can resolve to live a value-based life together, rather than running in a perpetual rat race.

OVERSERIOUSNESS: The whole world is full of seriousness. As a child, one is asked by one's parents over and again, "When will you become serious?" As an adult if you want to be joyful at times, people will say, "Don't behave like a child! Life is serious, death is serious." There is a lot of seriousness in hospitals and religious places. There is no laughter at work places and newspapers and television programmes are continually bombarding us with bad news and negative thoughts, which make people even more insecure. At a tender age, children are being loaded with information. Instead of basket ball they are playing computer games and

This is how a typical Laughter Club looks like in India

chess, where you need to apply a lot of thought and there is practically no laughter. Already children of today are behaving like young adults. People are becoming more logic-oriented, they look for logic in laughter too. The very essence of laughter is absurdity. Where there is logic, there is no laughter.

We are already paying a heavy price for taking life too seriously and now the time has come to take laughter seriously. We are trying to break the seriousness of life through Laughter Clubs and revive the spirit of laughter and bring it back as a way of life.

CONDITIONAL LAUGHTER AND HAPPINESS: Why can children laugh more than 300-400 times a day and adults only 15 times? This is because children have not decided upon any conditions for their laughter. They laugh because they want to laugh and are joyful. As we grow older, we start setting conditions for our laughter and happiness. If I get this, I will laugh. Only if I get a job of my liking am I happy. So on and so forth. We are therefore always looking for some reason to laugh. Today there are very few situations which really make us laugh, but there are hundreds of things which can make us unhappy. The Laughter Club is a joint effort of like-minded people to liberate laughter and happiness from reason. We all decide to be happy, irrespective of what happens in our lives.

EXPENSIVE MODERN MEDICINE: There is no substitute for modern medicine as it can save people from the very clutches of death. The results of surgery are unmatched. Life expectancy has increased significantly because of advanced medical, surgical and diagnostic techniques. However, despite research and development, the incidence of heart disease, blood pressure, allergic disorders, psychosomatic disorders and cancer is rising, obviously because of stress. For most people in developing countries, modern medical treatment is becoming expensive and beyond their reach. A major part of their income is spent on treating stress-related diseases. A wonder medicine like laughter can save on medical expenses by strengthening the immune system, which plays a key role in preventing a large number of diseases.

CHAPTER - 3

How did the Idea of Laughter Clubs Originate?

In March, 1995, I thought of writing an article on 'Laughter - the Best Medicine' for 'My Doctor' a health magazine that I edited. When I found a large amount of scientific literature on the benefits of laughter on the human mind and body, I was amazed that very few people laugh and smile in Mumbai. I was very impressed by American journalist Norman Cousins' book 'Anatomy of an Illness' in which he described how he laughed his way out of an incurable disease of the spine - Ankylosing Spondylitis. I also read about the research work done by Dr. Lee S. Berk from Loma Linda University, California, who showed how mirthful laughter reduced the stress hormone levels in the body and the effects of laughter on the immune system.

Early morning at 4 a.m. on 13th March 1995, I was walking up and down in my living room and suddenly an idea flashed into my mind: If laughter is so good why not start a Laughter Club? Then I decided not to

Dr. Madan Kataria at his Mumbai clinic.

publish the article, but instead I went to a public park at Lokhandwala Complex, Andheri, in Mumbai and spoke to people about starting a Laughter Club. The remarkable thing about this idea was that I conceived it at 4 a.m. in the morning and within 3 hours a plan was put into action.

So, exactly at 7 a.m. I started speaking to people who were taking their morning walk about the idea of starting a Laughter Club. Initially people laughed at the idea and asked if I was OK. They thought I was kidding or had gone crazy. Out of four hundred people walking in the park, I motivated four people to start laughing, standing in one corner of the park. People laughed at the concept and ridiculed the idea, but when the health benefits were explained, many got interested and the attendance started growing. The participants were mostly men aged forty plus, as well as some women and children.

In the beginning, all the participants stood in a circle and I would invite someone to come to the center and crack a joke or tell a humorous anecdote. People enjoyed the fun and felt nice after 10-20 minutes of laughter every morning. This method worked fine for about 15 days, after which the stock of good jokes ran out. Stale jokes, jokes targeted at a particular community, hurtful jokes and dirty jokes began to come up, which embarrassed many members, especially the women. It was evident that if we wanted to laugh every day we could not depend on someone telling jokes 365 days a year. Jokes were banned and it was decided that the club members would laugh without them.

HOW TO LAUGH WITHOUT JOKES: Most members found it difficult to laugh for no reason. After a lot of thinking and soul searching I came up with an action plan to help people laugh without jokes and did some basic research. The biggest hurdles preventing one from laughing are inhibition and shyness. To remove these, the group members were told to gather in large numbers. The larger the group, the easier it is to laugh. Laughter initiated in a large group is contagious and people start laughing looking at each others' faces. Every member would raise his hands up towards the sky while laughing, which is an easier posture for laughing and makes one feel less inhibited. Each laughing session starts with a deep breathing exercise. Members stretch their hands upwards and take a deep breath, hold it for some time and then gradually exhale. This breathing exercise is similar to '*Pranayam*' in Yoga, which helps in increasing the vital capacity of the lungs and helps in producing laughter. After deep breathing everybody starts chanting Ho-Ho, Ha-Ha-Ha. Slowly increasing the speed of Ho-Ho, Ha-Ha-Ha, they suddenly burst into hearty laughter by stretching their hands up and looking at each others' faces. Each kind of laughter lasts for about 20-30 seconds. This Ho-Ho, Ha-Ha-Ha exercise is akin to a yogic exercise called '*Kaphalbhati*' where there is a rhythmic movement of the diaphragm and abdominal muscles. It helps to facilitate the lungs in order to initiate laughter.

When a large number of people gather in a group and chant Ho-Ho, Ha-Ha-Ha, it charges the whole atmosphere with laughter. Since everyone can easily participate in this exercise, each one feels a sense of achievement. This was another step towards removing the members' inhibitions.

LAUGHING AT THE SAME TIME: All the members were instructed to laugh at the same time, following the instructions of an anchor person who conducted the session. The anchor person gave his command 1..2...3. If all the members start laughing at the same time, the effect is good.

EYE CONTACT - THE KEY: While laughing, we discovered that if we look into the eyes of the neighbour and start laughing, something happens to the other person and he too starts laughing. The participants are instructed to look at each others' faces, as everyone has a peculiar style of laughing. This helps to enhance the stimulus and generate natural laughter.

Over a period of 15 days, a few more types of laughter were created like laughing with the mouth wide open, no-sound laughing, beginning with lips closed and little humming sounds, medium laughter and cocktail laughter. To avoid boredom, a variety of stimulated laughter has been introduced, based on yoga. This also helped to promote playfulness among the participants. In other words, it is not at all difficult to laugh without jokes if laughter is practised in a group.

CHAPTER - 4

The Right Time and Place for Laughter Sessions

What is the right time to hold a laughter session? "Can I hold a session in the evenings after I return from work?" "Must I go to a public park for my daily guffaws?" "Can't I just laugh alone at home?" These are common queries from people, who want to be a part of the laughter movement. You may laugh at any time of the day, but to laugh in a group in a new yogic way, you will first have to join a group to gain a feel of the concept. Once you understand the concept and learn the various techniques then it may be possible to laugh with 2-3 people anywhere, or may be you can laugh alone at home. But to gain the maximum benefits, you must laugh in a group most of the time and in between you may try laughter with one or two people in a family.

Laughter Yoga has two types of laughter activities. First, laughter yoga exercises where a group of people laugh as a form of workout based on yoga and then indulge in playfulness which helps the participants to laugh

spontaneously. This type of laughter practice can be done outdoors in a public park or beach, or indoors. These exercises are done standing and there is lot of movement, interaction and eye contact during the session.

The second type of activity is called Laughter Meditation, in which you don't have to make any effort to laugh. Real laughter which is much deeper and more spontaneous flows out of your body like a fountain. It is highly contagious and very profound. You will experience laughter coming out of your whole being. Laughter Meditation cannot be done outdoors because it needs silence and concentration. Therefore, it can only be done indoors sitting on the floor and lying on your back with the eyes closed.

IDEAL TIME

Ideally, a laughing session must take place in the morning, especially in India where weather conditions are very favourable for people to take a morning walk. In India we laugh 365 days in a year and 30 days in a month. Most Laughter Club meets are held in public parks where people enjoy their walks and have laughter sessions also. In northern India, the attendance becomes thin in winter, but still many who are regular walkers, like to continue their sessions in winter too. Most clubs have their laughter sessions between 6 and 7 o'clock in the morning in open parks, according to the convenience of their participants. The total duration of deep breathing, laughter and stretching exercises should not exceed 15-20 minutes. Timing can be adjusted by a few minutes according to the suitability of particular groups and weather conditions, if done in an open place.

Why must one laugh in the morning? There are many reasons for this. It is always better to start the day with laughter. It keeps you in good spirits and in a good mood throughout the day. It energises you and 15-20 minutes of laughter carries its benefits throughout the day till you retire to bed. Though it is beneficial even if you laugh in the evenings, according to our experience, mornings are ideal. Many women in India could not come to morning laughter sessions as they were busy with their household tasks so they decided to set up Laughter Clubs in the evening. In Mumbai and Bangalore many such women's clubs have come up and they are very successful.

Another advantage of morning Laughter Clubs is that walking and laughter therapy sessions are complimentary to each other. Both take place in a public place and hence it is ideal for walkers to have a session either at the begining or at the end of their walks. As a matter of fact, I attribute the success of the Laughter Club movement to the selection of the right group of people, the morning walkers. They are health conscious people who can easily form a Laughter Club to add to their health-related activites. For those who come for a walk, laughter is a value addition to their exercise programme. Looking back, if I had not started this concept with the morning walker, it would have failed for want of regular attendance. Morning walkers don't have to take special time out for a laughter session. There are already in public places. Therefore, by making laughter a part of your morning walk, you make the session a part of your routine without the bother of specially finding a particular time for laughing. Thus, the ritual become regular and you can get the benefits. Upon waking up the morning one's body is stiff. This is the right time to do stretching exercises. Some Laughter Clubs start with stretching exercises first, while people are still gathering. Most yoga lovers like to start with yogic postures at the time of sunrise. So the practice of *hasya yoga* or Laughter Therapy is started at about the same time. Pollution is least in the morning in big cities. During a laughter session at a public park in the open, you will get the freshest air you are likely to get throughout the day. This is an added benefit you get when laughing in the morning.

In western countries, laughter sessions take place once a week or twice a week. Some groups meet once a fortnight. Somehow it is not possible to have laughter clubs going everyday. In future, when this concept is introuduced in the workplace there is the possibility of laughter sessions being held more often. Most clubs in western countries meet indoors and they spend 1-2 hours laughing, playing, sharing, dancing and meeting each other. These are called social laughter clubs.

In the workplace one can practice laughter sessions during tea/coffee breaks, lunch breaks or any time in the afternoon. Health clubs, yoga groups, Tai-chi groups, aerobic centres, sports groups and meditation centres can add 10-15 minutes of laughter as a value addition to their ongoing health building activity. The only precaution is that the laughter session should not take place immediately after lunch. There should be a gap of at least two hours after a meal.

CHAPTER - 5

What Happens During a Laughter Session?

HOW LAUGHTER CLUB MEMBERS STAND : All the members stand in a circle or semicircle, according to the space available, with the anchor person in the middle. He or she gives commands to initiate different types of laughter and exercises. The most important point to be noted here is that the members should not stand in a line to form a circle, as seen in military parades. The idea is that one should not feel conscious about breaking the circle or the line. It should be like a crowd format with people standing at random. The distance between members should not be more than 2-3 feet - the stretch of the arms - as members are supposed to look into each others' eyes and laugh. If the distance is more than this, the eye contact will not be effective enough to stimulate a person to laugh. Moreover, members should not stick to one place throughout the session. During each type of laughter, they should go up to different people and laugh with them with good sustained eye contact, or strike hands with each other whenever possible, depending upon the type of laughter. In the second format, the participants can stand in two groups facing each other. This format is more interactive and playful and helps to make the laughter more spontaneous and playful.

A typical laughter session is a perfect blend of various stimulated laughter techniques, interspersed with breathing and stretching exercises. A 20-30-minute laughter session can be divided into the following parts:

a) Rhythmic Clapping : This should be done with fully stretched arms. It is a warm-up exercise which stimulates accupressure points on the palms, helps to bring about a sense of well-being and builds energy levels.

b) Ho Ho Ha Ha Chanting : This is done in unison, along with clapping in a rhythm. It is based on dynamic yogic breathing techniques.

c) Deep Breathing : Slow and rhythmic breathing techniques with movement of the arms which help to bring about both physical and mental relaxation.

d). Yogic Laughter Techniques are developed from different yoga postures for physical well-being. For example, Hearty laughter, Lion laughter, Humming laughter, Gradient laughter etc.

e). Playful Laughter Techniques : The purpose is to help people become more playful, so that they can reduce their inhibitions and shyness. Playfulness also helps to convert stimulated laughter into spontaneous laughter. Some of the examples of playful laughter techniques are: One meter laughter, Milkshake laughter, Argument laughter, Mobile Phone laughter, Hot Soup laughter, Shy laughter, Swinging laughter, Dancing laughter, Spring Doll laughter and many more.

f). Value-based Laughter Techniques : Value-based laughter techniques are designed in such a way that we attach a special meaning to certain gestures made while laughing, so that our subconscious minds register its deep values, which helps to develop a positive attitude in daily life. For example, Appreciation laughter reminds us of how important it is to appreciate others in order to build a strong and harmonious relationship.

Western style greeting laughter : Shake hands look into the eyes of the other person and laugh.

Some of the value-based laughter techniques are Greeting laughter, Appreciation laughter, Forgiveness laughter, Shake Hands laughter, Hugging laughter, Guru laughter etc.

A 20-minute session is a perfect blend of stimulated laughter, deep breathing and stretching exercises. One bout of laughter lasts for 30 to 45 seconds. After each bout of laughter or sometimes after two bouts, two deep breaths are taken, in order to provide a break. This avoids exertion and tiredness. Sometimes, various neck, shoulder and arm stretching exercises are done in place of deep breathing between bouts of laughters.

Ho-Ho Ha-Ha-Ha Exercise : The session starts with a warm up Ho-Ho Ha-Ha-Ha exercise. All the members start chanting Ho-Ho Ha-Ha-Ha in unison, with rhythmic clapping 1-2, 1-2-3. (Ho-Ho; Ha-Ha-Ha). The sound should come from the navel, so as to feel the movement of abdominal muscles, while keeping the mouth half open. While chanting Ho-Ho Ha-Ha-Ha, a smile should be maintained, one should keep moving and meeting different people and maintain good eye contact.

Good movement and enthusiastic clapping will help to build up good energy levels (philosophy of motion creates emotion).

DEEP BREATHING : The session starts when one takes a deep breath through the nostrils and simultaneously raises the arms up towards the sky. The breathing in should be rhythmic, in accordance with the movements of the arms and one should keep on filling as much air as possible into the lungs and then hold one's breath for 4-5 seconds. Then the breath is released slowly and rhythmically by bringing the stretched arms back to normal position. One can breathe out through the nose or preferably through the mouth by pursing the lips, as if whistling silently. This is in accordance with yogic deep breathing (a type of *paranayama*) where the duration of exhalation is prolonged to almost double the time of inhalation.

Some anchor persons have added healing and helping words. For example while breathing in they say "Forgive" and they say "Forget" while breathing out. Other words which can be used are "Live" while breathing in and "Let Live" while breathing out. Some more slogans can be created by Laughter Club members like "we care" "we serve" etc. Anchor persons will say these words loudly, while all the members will say them in their minds during the breathing exercise. This is optional, not mandatory.

GREETING LAUGHTER : Again under the command of the anchor person, the members come a little closer to each other and greet each other with a particular gesture, while laughing in a medium tone and maintaining eye contact while moving around and meeting different people. One can shake hands and look into the eyes while laughing gently (western way of greeting). The Indian way of greeting is to join both the hands (*Namaste* laughter), or do *Aadaab* Laughter by moving one hand closer to the face (as Muslims greet each other), or one can bend at the hips and laugh by looking in the eyes of the neighbour (Japanese way). There could also be many other ways of greeting according to the region, state or country. This is followed by Ho-Ho Ha-Ha-Ha chanting and clapping 5-6 times and deep breathing twice.

HEARTY LAUGHTER : After the Ho-Ho Ha-Ha-Ha exercise, the first kind of laughter is hearty laughter. To initiate all kinds of laughter the

A laughter session (Hearty Laugh) at park in Ahmedabad (Gujarat), India.

anchor person gives a command 1,2,3... and everybody starts laughing at the same time. It builds up a good tempo and the effect is much better than it would be if different members laugh with different timings. In a hearty laugh, one laughs by throwing the arms up and laughing heartily. One should not keep the arms stretched up all the time during a hearty laugh. Keep the arms up for a while and bring them down and again raise them up. At the end of a hearty laugh, the anchor person starts clapping and chanting Ho-Ho Ha-Ha-Ha 5-6 times. That marks the end of a particular kind of laughter. This is followed by two deep breaths.

APPRECIATION LAUGHTER : This is a value-based laughter where the anchor person reminds the participants of how important it is to appreciate others. In this kind of laughter the tip of the index finger is joined with the tip of the thumb making a small circle while the hand is moved forward and backwards in jerks, looking at different members and laughing in a very gentle manner, as if you are appreciating your fellow beings in the group. It is followed by Ho Ho Ha Ha Ha chanting along with clapping.

ONE-METER LAUGHTER : This laughter is very playful and it duplicates how we measure an imaginary one meter. It is done by moving one hand over the stretched arm on the other side and extending the shoulder (like stretching to shoot with a bow and arrow). The hand is moved in three jerks by chanting Ae...., Ae....., Aeee..... and then participants burst into laughter by stretching both the arms and throwing the head a little backwards and laughing from the belly. (First the imaginary measurement is done on the left side and then on the right). This cycle is repeated twice. People enjoy the chanting of Ae... Ae.. in a staccato manner.

MILK SHAKE LAUGHTER : A recently introduced variation of one-meter laughter is milk shake laughter. Participants are asked to hold two imaginary glasses of milk or coffee and at the instruction of the anchor person the milk is poured from one glass into another by chanting Aeee....., and then pouring it back into the first glass by chanting Aeee... After that everyone laughs while making a gesture as if they are drinking milk. This process is repeated four times, followed by clapping while chanting Ho-Ho, Ha-Ha-Ha.

LION LAUGHTER : This particular laughter has been derived from a yogic posture known as *Simha Mudra* (Lion Posture). In the lion posture, the tongue is stuck out fully, while keeping the mouth wide open. With eyes wide open the hands are stretched like the paws of a lion and roaring like a lion is followed by laughter coming from the belly. Lion Laughter gives very good exercise to facial muscles, the tongue and throat. It removes inhibitions and is good for strengthening of the throat. It also improves blood supply to the thyroid gland.

SILENT LAUGHTER WITH MOUTH WIDE OPEN : In this type of laughter, the mouth is opened as wide as possible and participants laugh looking at each others' faces while making different gestures showing their palms to each other, while shaking their heads and sometimes their hands. Silent Laughter should be done with quick movements of the abdominal muscles, as we do during spontaneous laughter. It should not be like a prolonged hissing sound, which is more artificial.

Lion laughter is an adaptation of a yogic posture called *Simha mudra*.

IMPORTANT : One should not apply excess force or overexert while laughing without sound. It can be harmful if intra-abdominal pressure is raised unnecessarily. One should try to impart more feeling rather than apply more force.

HUMMING LAUGHTER WITH LIPS CLOSED : In this type of laughter, the lips are closed and a person tries to laugh while making a humming sound, which resonates throughout the skull. People can keep on looking at each other, making some gestures to stimulate each other. They can shake hands with each other or put in any other kind of playfulness. Some people also call it pigeon laughter.

CAUTION : One should not try to laugh without sound, while keeping the mouth closed with force. This raises undue pressure in the abdominal cavity which may be harmful.

SWINGING LAUGHTER : This is an interesting kind of laughter, as it has a lot of playfulness. All the members move outwards by two meters to widen the circle. On instruction from the anchor person people move

15 - Step New Model of a Laughter Therapy Session

DURATION :   20 - 30 minutes (maximum) Each bout of laughter should last for 30-40 seconds, followed by clapping and ho ho ha ha ha exercise. Take two deep breaths after every laughter.

STEP 1:   Clapping in a rhythm 1-2.........1-2-3
along with chanting of Ho-Ho........Ha-Ha-Ha

STEP 2:   Deep Breathing with inhalation through the nose and prolonged exhalation. (Along with healing words - Forgive, Forget; Live and Let Live)   (5 times)

STEP 3:   Shoulder, neck and stretching exercises
(5 times each)

STEP 4:   **Hearty Laughter** - Laughter by raising both the arms in the sky with the head tilted a little backwards. Feel as if laughter is coming right from your heart.

STEP 5:   **Greeting Laughter** - Joining both the hands and greeting in Indian style (Namaste) or shaking hands (Western Style) with at least 4-5 people in the group.

STEP 6:   **Appreciation Laughter** - Join your pointing finger with the thumb to make a small circle while making gestures as if you are appreciating your group members and laughing simultaneously.

STEP 7:   **One Meter Laughter:** Move one hand over the stretched arm of the other side and extend the shoulder (like stretching to shoot with a bow and arrow). The hand is moved in three jerks by chanting Ae...., Ae....., Aeee..... and then participants burst into laughter by stretching both the arms and throwing their heads a little backwards and laughing from the belly. (Repeat 4 times).

Milk Shake Laughter (a variation): Hold two imaginary glasses of milk or coffee and at the instruction of the anchor person pour the milk from one glass into the other by chanting Aeee...., and then pour it back into the first glass by chanting Aeee..., After that everyone laughs , while making a gesture as if they are drinking milk. (Repeat 4 times).

STEP 8:	**Silent laughter without sound** - Open your mouth wide and laugh without making any sound and look into each others' eyes and make some funny gestures.
STEP 9:	**Humming laughter with mouth closed** - Laughter with closed mouth and a humming sound. While humming keep on moving in the group and shaking hands with different people.
STEP 10:	**Swinging Laughter** - Stand in a circle and move towards the center by chanting Aee....Ooo....Eee...Uuu...
STEP 11:	**Lion Laughter** - Extrude the tongue fully with eyes wide open and hands stretched out like the claws of a lion and laugh from the tummy
STEP 12:	**Cell Phone Laughter:** Hold an imaginary mobile phone and try to laugh, making different gestures and moving around in the group to meet different people.
STEP 13 A :	**Argument Laughter:** Laugh by pointing fingers at different group members as if arguing.
STEP 13 B:	**Forgiveness/Apology Laughter:** Immediately after argument laughter catch both your ear lobes and laugh while shaking your head (Indian style) or raise both your palms and laugh as if saying sorry.
STEP 14:	**Gradient Laughter:** Gradient laughter starts with bringing a smile on the face, slowly gentle giggles are added and the intensity of laughter is increased further. Then the members gradually burst into hearty laughter and slowly and gradually bring the laughter down and stop.
STEP 15:	**Heart to Heart Laughter (Intimacy Laughter):** Come closer and hold each others hands and laugh. One can shake hands or hug each other, whatever feels comfortable.
CLOSING TECHNIQUE:	**Shouting 3 Slogans:** "We are the happiest person in this World" Y.........E.......S "We are the healthiest person in this World" Y.........E.......S "We are Laughter Club member " Y.........E.......S
Most Important:	In the end all the members should stand with their eyes closed for one minute with their arms spread upwards, hoping for world peace.

forward by making a prolonged sound of Ae... Ae... Aeeeee....., simultaneously raising the hands they all burst into laughter, while meeting in the center and waving their hands. After the bout of laughter, they move back to their original positions. The second time they move forward by saying Oh... Ooooooo.. and burst into laughter. Similarly, the third and fourth times they make the sounds of Eh... Eh... E.... and Oh... Oh... O... Many people are seen behaving like children and enjoying the fun.

CELL PHONE LAUGHTER : This is also known as mobile phone laughter. It is very amusing and playful. The participants hold imaginary mobile phones and try to laugh, while making different gestures and moving around in the group to meet different people and laugh as if they are enjoying the laughter. Mobile phone laughter can also be done in two groups facing each other and at the command of the anchor person both the groups cross each other while laughing and holding their mobile phones. If required, the two groups can cross over again to come back to their original positions. While crossing, the members must look at each other and laugh.

ARGUMENT LAUGHTER : This laughter is a competitive kind of laughter between two groups separated by a gap. Two groups look at each other and start laughing by pointing their index fingers at the members of the other group. Usually, the women are on one side and men on the other. This is also quite enjoyable and amusing.

FORGIVENESS/APOLOGY LAUGHTER : Immediately after argument laughter is the time for forgiveness laughter; the message behind this laughter is that if you fight with somebody you must apologise. How important it is to say sorry. In apology laughter participants hold both their ears lobes, by crossing the arms and they then bend at the knee and laugh.

GRADIENT LAUGHTER : This laughter is practised at the end of the session. All the members are asked to come closer to the anchor person. Gradient laughter starts with bringing smiles on faces and looking around at each other. Slowly, gentle giggles are added by the anchor person. Others follow and start giggling too. Slowly and gradually the intensity of laughter is increased even further and then the members gradually

Dynamic breathing exercise Ho-Ho Ha-Ha is practised just before
laughter meditation as a warm-up exercise

burst into hearty laughter. This goes on for about a minute. It is very refreshing and infectious.

HEART TO HEART LAUGHTER (INTIMACY LAUGHTER) : This laughter should be done last of all and here the participants come closer and hold each others' hands and laugh with compassionate eye contact. They can shake hands or hug each other, while laughing if they find it appropriate. This is also known as intimacy laughter. In conservative communities, ladies and gents can do this in separate groups.

CLOSING TECHNIQUE (POSITIVE AFFIRMATION AND PRAYER FOR WORLD PEACE) : At the end of the session three slogans are shouted. The anchor person delivers the first punchline by saying "We are the happiest people in the world". Everyone raises their arms and says. **Y-e-ee-s.** "We are the healthiest people in the world!" **Y-e-s.** "We are Laughter Club members!" **Y-e-e-s.** After the slogans all the members stretch their arms out towards the sky and close their eyes to pray for world peace. The standing in silence should last for 30 seconds to one minute.

43

LAUGHTER MEDITATION : In laughter yoga exercises we make an effort to laugh in a group, which soon becomes infectious. Laughter meditation is a state of mind, when one doesn't have to make an effort to laugh, but laughter flows out like a fountain without any reason. To reach the meditative stage of laughter, one needs to sit down on the floor and concentrate on dynamic breathing exercises. After that one needs to sit quietly and maintain continuous eye contact with others. Slowly laughter starts to emerge spontaneously. This meditation cannot be done outdoors. You need a quiet place to sit down in, a room without much disturbance. One can learn laughter meditation during our seminars and workshops.

NECK AND SHOULDER EXERCISES : Since there is some fatigue after completion of the first round, members need to take a break before starting the second round. Here, neck and shoulder exercises are done. They have been incorporated because cervical spondylosis, neck stiffness and frozen shoulders are common complaints after the age of forty.

BASIC GUIDELINES FOR A LAUGHTER SESSION

1. All the participants will start laughing at the same time, when the anchor person gives the command 1,2...start.

2. People should not stand far away from each other; to laugh without jokes, eye contact is the key. During each type of laughter, a person must maintain good eye contact with more than one of his neighbours.

3. Do not apply too much force while laughing, it should be more of a feeling and enjoying of the process.

CHAPTER - 6

Exercise in
Laughter Clubs

ost people living in cities lead sedentary lives. They use vehicles even for short distances. Sometimes I wonder when I see them waiting for more than five minutes for the lift to go to even the first or second floors. They expect their chauffeurs to drive the car right upto the doorstep. All this shows a lack of inclination to do exercise. This makes it difficult to stick to an exercise programme because one gets bored after sometime and abandons it. Being a physician, I treat a large number of patients for aches and pains, cervical spondylitis, backache and stiffness of joints, with a variety of pain killers. I am sure all these problems can be solved with regular exercise. I myself belong to an agricultural family. During my childhood in the countryside, I saw people working day and night, walking long distances in the fields. Rarely did they complain of aches and pains. They ate a lot of saturated fats, milk and milk products yet the incidence of hypertension and coronary artery disease was very low. My grandmother must have swallowed tons of oil and she died at the age of 104. I believe they could maintain good health because of plenty of exercise which was a part of their routine.

The introduction of exercises (these are described in some detail a little later) and deep breathing in between the different kinds of laughter had the desired effect. A small percentage of people who had stiff necks and frozen shoulders got rid of their painkillers. Some go to the extent of saying that the exercises have benefited them even more than laughter. And I have not heard anyone complaining of boredom, presumably because of the preceding or succeding laughter.

WALKING AND LAUGHING

Some have remarked that most Laughter Clubs seem to be located at places frequented by morning walkers. This is true. When I thought of starting Laughter Clubs, I could not think of a better place than a public park, where people go for a morning walk.

I thought morning walkers, being health conscious, would listen to anything conducive to good health. These are the people who are there everyday. One does not have to call them specially for a laugh. Looking back, it seems to me that selection of public parks for starting Laughter Clubs was appropriate and contributed substantially to the success of the laughter movement. If in the formative days of Laughter Clubs, I had to invite people specially for a laughter session, I am not too sure many would have turned up with regularity. Morning walkers were already enjoying the benefits of their walks and they didn't mind experimenting with laughter. It was like a value addition to their morning walks. Walk and laugh, laugh and walk has turned out to be a perfect combination. With the introduction of Laughter Clubs, those who were not regular, started walking without missing a single day And, those who come merely for laughter, by and large, could not resist the combination.

EXERCISING FACIAL MUSCLES

There are very few exercises designed for facial muscles. Due to constant frowning the skin develops wrinkles. Different types of laughter help to tone up the facial muscles. Laughter also improves the blood supply to the facial skin and brings a glow to it. Stretching of facial muscles contracts tear sacs to pour tears into the eyes which form a thin film and reflection of light in this film results in a shining spot in the eyes.

OTHER EXERCISES

After the laughter session is over, many people who have time, do exercises of the eyes, yogic deep breathing and chant *mantras* (religious hymns). Laughter groups have become very active and they have started organizing yoga camps, meditation courses, health talks and acupressure training classes. This all has happened because they are able to share a common platform - the Laughter Club.

NECK EXERCISES

Today neck pain is a very common complaint. Because of stress, bad posture, soft beds, or too many pillows, the muscles around the neck and shoulder go into spasm. Yoga gives a lot of importance to neck exercises, because all the major nerves and the spinal cord pass through the neck and control the whole body. Major blood vessels also pass through the neck and supply blood to the brain, which is the most important organ of the body.

Thus, the neck is like a bridge between the brain and the body. Everyday, in between various kinds of laughter the following neck exercises are done. By moving the neck towards right and left a pleasurable stretch is maintained for at least a few seconds. The neck is moved first from left to right and then up and down. People suffering from cervical spondylosis should not move the chin downwards. Instead, they should move up and then come to normal position. Lastly, the neck is rotated in a full circle, first from the left side and then from the right side.

CAUTION : Elderly people who feel giddy and uncomfortable while doing neck exercises, must refrain from these exercises and get themselves investigated by a qualified physician. Scores of people suffering from cervical spondylosis and neck pain have benefited from this exercise as they are able to maintain regularity by reason of exercising in a group.

SHOULDER EXERCISE

Place your fingertips on both shoulders and point both the elbows straight and move them slowly in a circle, backwards to forwards (anti-clockwise) five times and in reverse order (clockwise) five times. This exercise will ensure smooth movement of the shoulder joints. Due to a sedentary lifestyle, stress or diabetes, after a certain age people are prone to developing frozen shoulders. This exercise has both preventive and curative properties against frozen shoulder.

STRETCHING EXERCISES

Cross the fingers of both hands, bend a little from your waist, lift both hands while taking a long deep breath, stretch both the arms above your head, reverse the palms, stretch your full body and bend a little backwards. This stretching exercise prevents stiffness of the body. It stretches the muscles of the front portion of your body, keeps the spinal cord straight and relaxes the muscles of the entire back portion of the body. It can be repeated 2-3 times. The above three exercises are standard for every Laughter Club. There are a few optional exercises from among which, time permitting, a club can choose.

DURATION

The exercises during each laughter session can be introduced in between different types of stimulated laughter techniques. Exercises can be done at the beginning of the laughter session while members are gathering, or in-between various kinds of laughter to take a break, or in the middle of the session, as per the convenience of each particular group.

Every morning 1000 groups all over India meet in public parks to practice Laughter Yoga in a group. They combine Laughter exercises with yoga breathing.

Greeting Laughter (*Namaste* Laughter):
Join your hands and look into each other's eyes and laugh gently.

Hearty Laughter: Spread your arms up in the air with chin raised up and feel as if Laughter is coming right from your heart.

One-meter laugh: Measure an imaginary one meter by stretching one arm over the other and chant Aee....Aee.....Aee....Ha Ha Ha...Ha Ha Ha.

Mobile Laughter: Hold an imaginary mobile phone against your ear and laugh while interacting with other members of the group.

Guru Laughter : Put one hand over your head and say, "I learn from my mistakes Ha... Ha... Ha..."
Put the second hand over your head and say, "I learn from others' mistakes Ha... Ha... Ha..."

Milkshake Laughter: Hold two imaginary glasses of milk and mix them by saying Aee....Aeee.....Ah...ha...ha...

Gradient Laughter: Laugh slowly and gradually, start with a smile and then a little giggling, then chukling until your are laughing loud and heartily.

Hot Soup Laughter: Move your hands up and down as if you have had very hot and spicy soup and say Hee...Hee..Hee.

Shy Laughter: Hide your face behind your palms and look left and right towards various group members and laugh as if you are a shy person.

Heart to Heart laughter : Hug each other and laugh by feeling the vibrations in each other's bodies. Alternatively, you can hold hands and laugh.

Forgiveness Laughter: Catch your ear lobes and laugh as if you are saying sorry to each other. You can raise your hands and say sorry in western style.

Lion Laughter : Stick your tongue out fully, pose your hand like paws of the lion.
First roar like a lion and then laugh.

Arguement Laughter: Look at each other and wag your finger as if you are arguing and
laughing. This exercises can be done in two big groups facing each other.

Just Laugh: Somebody asked why are you laughing? We are just laughing for nothing said the Laughter Club member.

Laughter Meditation : When you don't have to make any effort to laugh and laughter flows out of your body like a fountain. Much more profound and deeper laughter.

Take a deep breath while stretching your arms up in the sky, hold the breath for 3-5 seconds and release. Repeat five times.

Shoulder exercise : Put your fingers on both your shoulders and try to draw an "O" with your elbows. There are also some neck stretching exercises in Laughter Clubs.

Prisoners laughing their anger out at a Mumbai prison.

Dr. Kataria teaching policemen how to laugh their stress away.

Members of a senior citizens home participating in a laughter session in Philadelphia USA.

Disabled children enjoying a laughter session in Perth, Australia.

A laughter session among school children in India.

Dr. Kataria laughing with a group of orphans in Chennai, South India.

A laughing session with blind school girls.

A laughing session at the National Association for the Blind in Mumbai, India.

Laughter session with Deaf and Dumb Children in Udaipur, India..

East meets West through Laughter: Dr. Kataria with Steve Wilson in USA.

Two Laughter Doctors meet in Italy: Dr. Kataria and Dr. Patch Adams.

Dr. Madan Kataria with Dr. Lee S Berk, a top researcher at
Loma Linda University, in California, USA

CHAPTER -7

For Whom is Laughter Therapy Unsuitable?

E ver since the inception of Laughter Clubs, there have been some people intrigued by the idea, but with a shade of doubt about its side or ill effects. This is especially so among cardiac patients and those who have undergone bypass surgery. Fortunately, there has not been even a single untoward incident in the history of the laughter movement. But, being a medical man, I am aware of the fact that people are instructed to force themselves to laugh and stimulate others to laugh. This involves some physical strain and a rise in intra-abdominal pressure. Some people, in order to get more benefits, become over enthusiastic and do forceful laughter by over straining themselves. While there are others who might have silent ailments with no obvious symptoms. It order to work out the various possibilities of side effects which might occur, I held discussions with a number of medical experts from various medical and surgical specialities. Thereafter, a list of ailments was worked

out and patients with these ailments were advised caution and medical advice prior to joining in at a laughter session.

HERNIA

Hernia is a protusion of abdominal contents - various parts of the intestine, usually the small intestine - through the weakened wall of abdominal muscles. In those who have undergone any abdominal surgery, the site of the incision becomes the weakest point. With a repeated increase in intra-abdominal pressure one might get an incisional hernia. Another common type of hernia occurs at the groin. The abdominal contents can protrude through the inguinal canal and produce a swelling in the groin area while coughing, sneezing and laughing. Elderly people are more prone to this condition because of muscles weakened by advancing age. Those suffering from a long-standing cough due to asthma or chronic bronchitis, should be extra careful because they are more prone to developing hernia. People with an enlarged prostate, who have to strain a lot while passing urine and those with chronic constipation are also susceptible to hernia.

The abdominal contents can also get pushed into the scrotal sac and cause swelling of the scrotum. This is also a variety of inguinal hernia known as indirect inguinal hernia. Another common site of hernia is at the umbellicus (navel). Some people do get a small umbellical hernia during childhood which progresses later on and becomes bigger. If someone gets a swelling on any part of the abdomen, or discomfort while laughing, they must get themselves examined by a general surgeon. The more susceptible people are those who have a chronic cough, an enlarged prostate, or chronic constipation.

If you have a hernia on one side, there is a possibility of developing it on the other side too. The best option is to have a periodic examination and not to apply undue force while laughing. At the same time, there is no need to be extra cautious or fearful about developing hernia. There are, in fact, more chances of herniation with coughing, sneezing and forceful expulsion in a constipated person than with laughter. I have not come across any persons who are enthusiastic laughers and have developed hernia. If diagnosed to be suffering from hernia, once surgical correction is done, one should be assessed by a surgeon for fitness before attending laughter therapy.

ADVANCED PILES (HAEMORRHOIDS)

Those suffering from piles with active bleeding, or those at a stage when piles protrude from the anus, should not join the laughter session, as these conditions may worsen with increase of intra-abdominal pressure. The patient may join a Laughter Club once surgical or other type of treatment is taken.

HEART DISEASES WITH CHEST PAIN

People suffering from anginal chest pain should not join laughter sessions, without consulting their physicians or preferably a cardiologist. But heart patients who are doing well on medication and those who have had heart attacks in the past and record a Stress Test (treadmill test) within normal limits can join the sessions without any problem. Even those who have undergone bypass surgery can participate in laughter if their treadmill test results are fine. In a nutshell, if you are allowed to take a basic walk for 45 minutes, you can definitely join a laughter session. Avoid laughter therapy for at least three months after a heart attack or coronary artery bypass surgery.

RECENT SURGERY

To be on the safe side, one should not join a laughter session, within three months of any major operation, especially on the abdomen. In the later case, one must get a go-ahead from one's surgeon.

UTEROVAGINAL PROLAPSE

In some women, ligaments supporting the uterus become weak after the age of 40. Downward sagging of the uterus occurs, causing discomfort in the lower abdomen. One of the signs of such prolapse is involuntary passage of urine while coughing, sneezing and laughing. Such women should avoid laughter sessions until they are treated surgically.

PREGNANCY

In a small percentage of pregnant women, there is a possibility of abortion if there is a repeated rise in intra-abdominal pressure and they should avoid laughter sessions, till some conclusive data is available, after conducting research on the effects of laughter on pregnancy.

ATTACKS OF COLD AND FLU

Acute viral infections are highly contagious and if a person with such an infection laughs, he is likely to spread the infection by way of droplets in the air. People should stay away for about a week once they catch a cold. The good news is that regular laughter therapy increases the resistance of the upper respiratory mucous membrane and people are getting fewer coughs and colds, as shown by a recent survey done in the first phase of clinical research on Laughter Clubs.

RULING OUT TUBERCULOSIS

Tuberculosis is rampant in India and there is a possibility of spraying out bacteria while laughing in open cases of tuberculosis. Through the anchor persons, a vigil is kept on participants who have a cough for more than 10 days. In such cases, a chest X-ray, sputum and bloods tests are recommended to rule out the possibility of tuberculosis. Fortunately, there has not been even a single case of tuberculosis among more than 20,000 Laughter Club members all over the country. But we can't take this for granted and proper medical supervision is a must. Keeping a handkerchief or tissue handy is highly recommended for those who are prone to getting phlegm while laughing, especially those with chronic bronchitis, smokers or asthmatics.

EYE COMPLICATIONS

Any person with high intra-ocular pressure (glaucoma) or with a history of rational or vitreous hemorrhage should take the opinion of an ophthalmologist before joining a Laughter Club.

ANY OTHER DISCOMFORT

Even members without any ailment who experience discomfort during a laughter session, should discontinue their attendance and consult a doctor. If there is no problem, probably there is something wrong with the laugher's technique. We are holding regular anchor person training programmes to improve upon the techniques of laughter therapy.

CONCLUSION

All the don'ts stated above should not scare away a person and deprive him of the beneficial effects of this wonderful nature cure, but caution should be observed against any untoward effects of laughter. We are setting questionnaires for all Laughter Club members, to gather vital information about the physical health of the participants and screen vulnerable groups. We are also making periodical announcements and sending circulars to make people aware of various precautions that they must take while participating in laughter therapy.

CHAPTER - 8

Health Benefits of Laughter Therapy

I t is more than six years now, since the first 'Laughter Club' was set up. There is a growing demand for opening such clubs at many more places in India and abroad. Almost every day more and more people are joining Laughter Clubs and are being benefited. One of the reasons for these benefits is of course that laughter puts the members in a positive frame of mind and gradually makes them positive thinkers.

People suffering from a variety of stress-related diseases have benefited in some way or the other. But we don't claim that long-standing ailments have been cured by laughter therapy. Laughter is more of a supplementary and preventive therapy. We are starting clinical research on it very soon. It will take a couple of years before we are in a position to publish some very authentic research data on laughter therapy.

Dr. Kataria sharing a laugh with a child in a hospital in Perth, Australia.

ANTI STRESS

Laughter is one of the finest, most economical and easy to practice anti-stress measures. Laughter is one of the best muscle relaxants. Laughter expands blood vessels and sends more blood to the extremities and other muscles all over the body. A good bout of laughter also reduces the levels of stress hormones epineprine and cortisol. It can be said to be a form of dynamic meditation or relaxation.

For meditation, one has to put in a concerted effort to completely detach oneself, on mental and emotional levels, from one's own feelings and thought processes, as well as from the physical world to prevent distractions. On the other hand, while laughing, we do not have any conscious thought process and all our senses naturally and effortlessly combine in a moment of harmony, to give joy, peace and relaxation. In other types of meditation you need to concentrate a lot to take your mind away from distracting thoughts, which is easier said than done. Therefore, laughter is, if I may say so, the easiest form of meditation and one which brings you instant relaxation.

STRENGTHENS THE IMMUNE SYSTEM

The immune system plays a most important role in maintaining good health and keeping away infections, allergies and cancers. It has been proved by psychoneuroimmunologists that all negative emotions like anxiety, depression or anger weaken the immune system of the body, thereby reducing its fighting capacity against infections. According to Dr. Lee S. Berk from Loma Linda University, California, USA, laughter helps to increase the count of natural killer cells (NK cells - a type of white cell) and also raises the antibody levels. Researchers have found that after laughter therapy there is an increase in antibodies (Immunoglobulin A) in the mucous of the nose and respiratory passages, which is believed to have a protective capacity against some viruses, bacteria and other micro organisms. There are many members of Laughter Clubs who have noticed that the frequency of common colds, sore throats and chest infections has decreased. The effect of laughter on the immune system is considered to be very significant with regard to deadly diseases like AIDS and cancer.

BEST AEROBIC EXERCISE

The one benefit almost everybody derives is a sense of well-being. After 15 minutes of laughter in the morning, they feel fresh throughout the day. There is no medicine like laughter, which gives you such an instant result. The reason for the sense of well-being is that you inhale more oxygen while laughing. Laughter can be compared to any aerobic exercises except you don't have to wear fancy shoes or clothes. You don't need to sweat hard on the jogging tracks. According to Dr. William Fry from Standford University, one minute of laughter is equal to 10 minutes on the rowing machine. In other words, laughter stimulates heart and blood circulation and is equivalent to any other standard aerobic exercise. Laughter exercise is suited for sedentary people and those who are confined to a bed or wheelchair.

DEPRESSION, ANXIETY AND PSYCHOSOMATIC DISORDERS

The stress and strain of modern life are taking a heavy toll of the human mind and body. Mind-related diseases like anxiety, depression, nervous

Lion laughter in the Dubai desert: Dr. Kataria with Ram, Gautam and family.

breakdowns and sleeplessness are on the rise. Laughter has benefited many people who were on heavy anti-depressant pills and tranquillizers. Now they are getting better sleep and their depression has reduced. People with suicidal tendencies have started living with more hope.

High Blood Pressure and Heart Disease

There are a number of causes for high blood pressure and heart disease like heredity, obesity, smoking and excessive intake of saturated fats. But stress is one of the major factors. Laughter definitely helps to control blood pressure by reducing the release of stress-related hormones and bringing relaxation.

In experiments it has been proved that there is a drop of 10-20 mm. pressure after participating for 10 minutes in a laughter session. It does not mean that those who are taking 2-3 tablets for blood pressure every-day will be completely cured. Maybe, you will require 2 tablets if you are taking 3, or borderline high blood pressure patients may not require any medication after some time. It takes years to develop high blood pressure. It cannot be reversed in a few days or a month. But definitely laughter will exercise some control and arrest further progress of the disease. Similarly, if you are at high risk of developing heart disease, laughter could be the best preventive medicine. Those who are suffering from heart disease and have stabilized on medication will find that laughter improves the blood circulation and oxygen supply to the heart muscles. Due to improvement of blood circulation there are less chances of forming a clot. Those who have had heart attacks or have undergone bypass surgery can also participate in a Laughter Club's laughter therapy.

NATURAL PAIN KILLER

Laughter increases the levels of endorphins in our bodies, which are natural pain killers. Norman Cousins, an American journalist who was suffering from an incurable disease of the spine, was benefited by laughter therapy when no painkiller could help him. Endorphins released as a result of laughter may help in reducing the intensity of pain in those suffering from arthritis, spondylitis and muscular spasms of the body. Many women have reported a reduced frequency of migraine headaches.

ALLEVIATES BRONCHITIS AND ASTHMA

Laughter is one of the best exercises for those suffering from asthma and bronchitis. It improves the lung capacity and oxygen levels in the blood. Doctors recommend chest physiotherapy to bring out mucous (phlegm) from the respiratory passages. Blowing forcefully into an instrument and blowing balloons is one of the common exercises given to asthmatics. Laughter does the same job, more easily and almost free of cost. There are many individuals suffering from asthma and bronchitis who are members of Laughter Clubs. They have reported a reduced frequency of their attacks. Laughter Therapy may cause some discomfort if you have severe bronchospasm. There is a small percentage of asthma cases who may get a little aggravation by doing any exercise (exercise induced asthma). Such individuals should consult their doctors before taking up Laughter Therapy. One of the most common causes for frequent attacks of asthma is infection. Laughter Therapy increases the antibody levels in the mucous membranes of the respiratory passages, thereby

Laughter Club of Ghatkopar (E) in Mumbai, India.

reducing the frequency of chest infections. It also tones up the normal mucous clearing system of the bronchial tubes. Stress is another factor, which can bring on an attack of asthma. By reducing stress, laughter can improve the prognosis of the disease.

IMPROVES STAMINA IN ATHLETES

Since breathing capacity is one of the factors which determines stamina in sports, laughter before any competitive sports activity will increase the relaxation levels and hence, performance. Laughter, I think, can be beneficially introduced as a regular exercise in any kind of sports activity.

INTERNAL JOGGING

There are plenty of exercises available for your muscles, but laughing provides a good massage to all internal organs. It enhances their blood supply and increases their efficiency. It has been compared to magic fingers, which reach into the interior of the abdomen and massage the organs. The best massage it gives is to the intestines. It improves the blood supply and helps the bowels to move properly.

Good for Actors and Singers

Laughter Therapy can be very beneficial for singers and actors. Increased lung capacity and exercise of the diaphragm and abdominal muscles will help to gain better control over speech. Another benefit would be enhanced self-confidence and reduced stage fright due to an increase in the body's relaxation level, which results from laughter.

Makes You Look Younger

People do exercise for all the muscles of the body, but there is no regular exercise designed for facial muscles except in Yoga. Laughter is an excellent exercise for your facial muscles. It tones up the muscles of the face and improves facial expressions. When you laugh, your face becomes red due to an increase in blood supply, which nourishes the facial skin and makes it glow. Laughing people look more cheerful and attractive. By squeezing the tear glands through laughter, it moistens the eyes adding a little sparkle to them. Laughter exercises the abdominal muscles and helps to improve muscle tone of those with pot bellies.

Interpersonal Relationships

Laughter brings people together and improves interpersonal relationships. All the members of a Laughter Club meet each other with open minds and they care for each other. You will get a chance to interact with a number of people with a positive frame of mind. Today, members of different Laughter Clubs are like family members. They know each other well; they share their griefs and sorrows. They share their joyful moments too, by meeting each other, going out for picnics etc. They organize health workshops, yoga camps and naturopathy seminars from time to time. People from various walks of life come together and greet each other with smiling faces.

Self Confidence Through Laughter

When you are laughing in a group at a public place with your arms up towards the sky, it removes your inhibitions and over a period of time you become a more sociable, unreserved and outgoing person. Admittedly, some people are initially a bit reluctant to join the laughter group, in spite of a strong inclination towards doing so, for fear of appearing absurd to onlookers. However, this is a passing phase and the very decision to join a Laughter Club opens your mind. Gradually, it also adds to your self confidence. It will also help to develop your personality and leadership qualities.

SOCIAL BENEFITS OF LAUGHTER

Ongoing research shows that people suffering from depression are more prone to many illnesses like high blood pressure, heart disease and cancer. Depression also affects the immune system adversely. Common causes of depression are social isolation and a diminishing family value system. These are more pronounced in western countries but are now slowly affecting the east also. Laughter Clubs have helped many people to get rid of their antidepressant pills in a short period of time. The magic which has worked wonders is the friendship and brotherhood gained from Laughter Clubs. Laughter Clubs are fast developing into close-knit communities. With the spread of Laughter Clubs in every locality, each club has taken the shape of a small community, wherein its members experience a sense of affiliation and belonging to the group. Laughter Clubs are turning into large "Laughing Families".

CHAPTER - 9

Global Laughter Movement: The Happy-demic Spreads

From just five persons in March 1995, Laughter Clubs have spread all over the world like a happy-demic (the word coined by my friend Dr. Dale Anderson from Minnesota, USA). At present there are more than 1200 Laughter Clubs in India, USA, U.K, Australia, Denmark, Sweden, Norway, Germany, France, Switzerland, Italy, Singapore, Malaysia, Dubai and many other countries. Every day I receive enquiries from all over the world to set up Laughter Clubs. Why is this laughter movement spreading like a wild fire?

There are some reasons which make laughing without a reason acceptable to the common man. Some of the reasons behind the success of the laughter movement are: a) Never before in history has laughter been so well structured and made an organised exercise routine to be practised by the common man. This practice promotes instant relaxation from stress and has helped scores of people worldwide derive health benefits.

Laughter Club in Gubbio, Italy.

b) Everybody knew about laughter being the best medicine but nobody had an idea of how to bring more laughter into their lives. Humour and jokes are not working enough and there are not many happenings in life which make us really laugh. Also, there is a problem about an appropriate time to laugh and people rely more and more on a sense of humour which is not very common.

There was a strong need for a platform on which people could laugh without bothering about a sense of humour. People were looking for such a platform where there is a commitment to laughter. I think people have found everything they wanted in a Laughter Club. They are laughing because they want to laugh, they are celebrating life, they are having fun and cultivating playfulness. c) This idea of laughing without a reason is universal and can connect people all over the world without any language barriers. d) A Laughter Club is a practical platform where one can actually practice laughter rather than just talk about laughter. Everyone is encouraged to find their own laughter rather than look for someone who could make them laugh. e) It is an ideal platform for people to connect with each other, socialise and cultivate fellowship. This has helped many people to overcome their depression and isolation. f) The unique feature of Laughter Clubs is that laughter is free. Laughter Clubs constitute a social movement which is non-political, non-religious and non-profit making. We have not kept any membership fee for Laughter Clubs. g) A group laughter exercise, it is easy to practise and gives benefits which are the same as those gained from real laughter. People are opening up and finding their sense of humor through laughter. h) This particular way of laughing is free from any kind of negativity, associated with negative humor. i) This is a short and sweet 10-20 minute exercise, which can be a value addition to other health building activities like yoga, meditation, aerobics, Tai-Chi, etc.

THE BEGINING WAS TOUGH

Going down memory lane, I recall how it all started for fun and I never dreamt it would become such a big movement. During the formative days it was quite difficult for me to get started. People were afraid of being laughed at if they joined the group. The first to object were a few representatives of the garden authorities in the suburb of Mumbai where we started the first Laughter Club. They thought it would be a public nuisance and noise pollution and advised me to discontinue. However, I persisted and I went around motivating people. It was after a few talks by me on the health benefits of laughter that people started coming forward. Still many ridiculed the idea and called us a *"Murakh Mandli"* ("Band of Fools") in our local language.

There were about 300-400 people walking in that park every day but only 15-20 people joined initially. When they started enjoying a sense of well-being after the sessions, more and more people trickled in. This made the park authorities soften their stand and they allowed the group to go on with the activity. Soon, the number swelled to 55-60 including a few women. Initially, we laughed at jokes but that didn't work after some time. We learnt the art of laughing without jokes by inventing a variety of stimulated kinds of laughter.

PASSER-BY REACTIONS

The very idea of laughing in a public place without any reason sounded intriguing to many people who saw about 50 people engaged in what they perceived as a funny activity. Scores of people used to watch us from balconies of adjoining buildings and roadsides and the hundreds who walked inside the park couldn't resist staring as they passed us. The initial reaction of most of these people was amusement and surprise. The question in their minds was: How can they laugh in a public place without any reason? Some of those living around the park took half-hearted objection on the specious grounds of being woken up by the laughter. But that was largely for the psychological reason of opposition to anything new, even if it is for the better.

Among those watching from the roadside were youngsters who would watch the fun standing on the bridge nearby. They would respond with sounds of "Ho Ho Ha Ha" and then shy away from the scene. Many autorickshaw and taxi drivers who were not carrying any passengers would stop for a while and then proceed with shy smiles on their faces. Even bus drivers would slow down to get a glimpse of the laughing group. The good thing was that it amused most. But there were a few who raised their eyebrows and thought we were wasting our energy and disturbing others. Some of them passed sarcastic remarks. It must be said to the credit of those who laughed that they took all this as as a part of the game.

There were a few people who would stand a couple of yards away and keep watching the proceedings without gaining the courage to join in. Many who wanted to join the group would hold themselves back, thinking that there might be some fees to be paid before joining. Efforts were always made to clarify this impression. Membership of a Laughter Club involved neither filling up of any form, nor payment of any fee, nor any other fuss. Those who were slow to get into the spirit of the laughter expressed the opinion that it was artificial or forced. Those who practised daily found it beneficial and started to spread the news by word of mouth. Soon the concept caught on in the residential complex and many people would come just to watch these funny people in action. As we kept on updating our laughing techniques, people from adjoining localities also started coming and one fine day would express the desire to start similar clubs in their areas too. We were very happy to share the happiness. It was not more than two months from the start of the first Laughter Club that "Seven Bungalows", a nearby suburb of Mumbai, was resounding with the guffaws of the second Laughter Club.

MEDIA BREAKTHROUGH

The first media coverage of our Laughter Club was by India's most popular cultural show 'Surabhi' on the national television network. The production company has its office near the park where we had our laughter sessions every day. It tickled the curiosity of many newspapers and magazines all over the country. One fine day the news of Laughter Clubs hit the headlines of India's most popular English daily "The Times of India". The paper carried a picture of Laughter Club members on the front page with a report saying, "This club is not a laughing matter".

I was flooded with telephone calls and it created a flutter in the entire city. The effect was magical; our attendance went up by 50%. Requests from other areas started pouring in. Within 3 months there were 16 clubs! Lokhandwala Public Park became a famous hunting ground for journalists from various newspapers, magazines and national and international television networks. Our first international exposure was on BBC News followed by coverage on CNN and NHK (Japan). I have not seen such enthusiastic media coverage for any other social movement. Soon, I lost count of the frequency with which the laughter movement appeared in some national or international paper or magazine.

It did not take very long for the movement to spread outside Mumbai. Madhuri and I started travelling all over India on invitation and helping people to start Laughter Clubs. I ignored my medical practice and my wife Madhuri was not really laughing without money because we did not charge anybody for the Laughter Clubs. Somehow we carried on and Laughter Clubs multiplied at an astronomical pace. Today we have more than 1000 Laughter Clubs all over India in cities like Mumbai, Bangalore,

Hundreds of people walking on the road in Pune, India, at the
World Laughter Day celebrations in May 2000.

Pune, Nasik, Chennai, Kolkata, Hyderabad, Goa, Ahmedabad, Baroda,
Raipur, Delhi and many more. Every day new clubs are being opened
and many yoga groups are adding laughter yoga to their yoga routines. In
India most Laughter Clubs meet in the morning at public places, but
there are some evening women clubs and clubs in offices and factories,
schools, blind schools, disabled children's schools and old age homes.

THE LAUGHTER MESSAGE GOES OVERSEAS

Some Indians settled abroad, while on a holiday to their homeland,
were impressed by the idea and felt that it could be effective in terms of
social interaction. They took video films and also got acquainted with the
laughter techniques. They tried to establish Laughter Clubs in their places
of residence, but their efforts did not make much headway. Still there is
a great deal of interest in Laughter Clubs abroad due to the awareness
created by the media. The *National Geographic* (May 1997 issue) carried
a double spread picture along with the message of Laughter Clubs. This
coverage was instrumental in spreading awareness of the concept all over

the world because of the magazine's wide readership. Hundreds of articles appeared in newspapers and magazines and the story of Laughter Clubs appeared on prominent televison networks all over the world. These include the *Los Angeles Times, Wall Street Journal, New York Times, The Daily Telegraph, ABC News* (Peter Jennings show), *BBC, CNN, NHK* (Japan), *ZDF* (Germany), *National TV* (in France and Belgium), *Channel 9* (Australia) and many others. I give major credit to the communication breakthrough of the 20th century - the Internet - which helped to spread the message of laughter to each and every corner of this planet. I travelled extensively in America, Europe, Middle East and the Far East along with my wife Madhuri and conducted seminars and workshops to train laughter leaders so that they could start their own Laughter Clubs.

LAUGHTER CLUBS IN USA

The United States of America was the first country outside India to start Laughter Clubs. The brain behind the US Laughter Club movement is Steve Wilson, a psychologist and America's joyologist. He had already written several books on humour, healing and positive work environments. Steve was planning a lecture tour to India in 1998, when he got a fax message from his father about the article which appeared in the *LA Times* about Laughter Clubs in India. He contacted me over the telephone and expressed his desire to meet me in Mumbai. We had instant rapport, like a brotherhood based on a mutual sense of urgency to disseminate information about the physical, mental, emotional and spiritual healing powers of laughter. Steve met me in Mumbai and we had conversations about laughter and we saw the enormous potential that existed in the systematic routine for laughing without using jokes under the guidance of a trained leader/motivator.

I took him to the Laughter Club at Juhu Beach in Mumbai and it was an exhilarating experience for Steve. He told me that I must go to America. In May 1999, Steve along with Karyn Buxman, a registered nurse and prominent humourist, organised a marathon laughter tour which covered the length and breadth of America. In one-and a-half months we visited 14 cities and conducted about 25 seminars and workshops. People in

Gabriela from Switzerland with Susan from Denmark doing milk-shake laughter.

USA loved the new idea and a number of articles appeared in newspapers, magazines, radio and television networks. We made appearances in cities like New York, New Jersey, Phoenix, Louisville, Minneapolis, San Jose, Philadelphia, Boca Raton, St. Petersburg and Columbus (Ohio) which was the base where we started the world laughter tour. We were house guests of the Wilsons and spent time laughing and exchanging ideas, information and visions while appreciating each other's cultures.

The World Laughter Tour seemed to take on a life of its own, gaining momentum on a daily basis. With Pam (Steve's wife), always at his side, and Karyn being his strongest supporter, Wilson had gotten the laughter ball rolling. Here are just some of the developments, and the people who helped, with apologies because we are bound to omit the names of important supporters in this short synopsis.

The first USA Laughter Club was established even prior to the lecture tour, by Jenni Reusser, at the YMCA in Orrville, Ohio. The first USA Laughter Club in a nursing home was established in Canton, Ohio, and then the first club in an elementary school in the same city, thanks to

Peggy Stabholtz and Nancy Engle. Steve and Pam organised several laughter leader training programmes across America and that helped people to start their laughter clubs. Steve's website www.worldlaughtertour.com attracted heavy traffic, providing information and assistance for training leaders and setting up Laughter Clubs. Steve also trained many laughter leaders from Canada and some from Europe and Australia, helping the movement spread further. More information about US Laughter Clubs is available on www.worldlaughtertour.com

LAUGHTER CLUBS IN GERMANY

In March 1998, Henz Tobler a young man from Wiesbaden came to Mumbai to learn about Laughter Clubs. He visited different clubs in Mumbai and learnt some of the laughter yoga exercises. He mentioned to me that many people in Germany had read about Indian Laughter Clubs in newspapers and magazines. In October 1998, he demonstrated some of the laughter yoga techniques at the Humour Conference held in Basel, Switzerland. He displayed photographs of various Laughter Club activities during the conference. I was invited as a speaker to the Humour Conference in Basel, Switzerland in October 2000 and conducted a day-long workshop on Laughter Yoga. The conference was attended by more than 600 participants from all over the world, with the most participants being from Switzerland and Germany. This helped to spread the message of Laughter Clubs in Germany. At that conference I got the privilege to meet eminent German psychologist Micheal Titze, who had worked on laughter and humour for many years. We shared thoughts and he endorsed the philosophy behind Laughter Clubs.

I also got an opportunity to meet Micheal Burger, a businessman and philanthropist from Wiesbaden. I was very much impressed by his love and passion for laughter and humour. He invited me to Wiesbaden to conduct a 2-day laughter workshop for a group of 30-35 people. This workshop was held at a church called "Humour Church" which is being used to promote laughter and humour activities. In that group, a dynamic woman named Gudula Steiner Junker was trained as a laughter leader and started the Wiesbaden Laughter Club. She is running the Laughter Club

A laughter session at a workshop in Hamburg, Germany.

very successfully. Some participants from Wiesbaden workshop thereafter started Laughter Clubs in Berlin, Frankfurt and other cities of Germany.

HAMBURG LAUGHTER CLUBS

Robert W.L.Butt, a young dynamic English teacher came to Mumbai for personalised training and he is the founder of the Hamburg Laughter Club. He invited my wife Madhuri and me to Hamburg to do a laughter workshop in 2001 and again in February 2002. Thanks to Robert's hard work, awareness of Laughter Clubs in Hamburg was enhanced by attracting media attention and there were many articles in newspapers as well as television coverage. He has established Dr. Kataria's School of Laughter Yoga in addition to his weekly laughter meetings.

WORLD LAUGHTER DAY CELEBRATIONS IN GERMANY

In the month of May 2001, World Laughter Day was also celebrated in Berlin at Alexander's Square. Inspite of bad weather, hundreds of people turned up for the celebrations and held a laughter session along with prayers for world peace.

In May 2002, a humour conference was organised in Stuttgart. It was attended by more than 2000 participants and the Laughter Club idea was highlighted during the conference. Many Laughter Club members from all over Germany attended the World Laughter Day celebrations on 6th May, 2002. I have not been to other cities of Germany but I am very well aware that there are more than 35 Laughter Clubs all over the country. I receive e-mails from the laughter leaders and some day I will surely visit them all.

Laughter Movement in Denmark

Jan Thygesen Poulsen, the President of the Laughter Club International - Denmark Chapter, saw an article in a Danish newspaper in 1998 about the World Laughter Day celebrations in Mumbai where thousands of people laughed for world peace. He contacted me on e-mail and expressed his desired to organise a similar mega event by gathering together thousands of Danes in Copenhagen. In January 2000, Jan single-handedly gathered nearly 10,000 people in the Town Hall Square and laughed with them. It went into the Guiness Book of Records!

After his phenomenal success he decided to lead the laughter movement all over Denmark. I have visited Copenhagen several times to conduct workshops and training programmes. Now we have more than 40 Laughter Clubs all over Denmark. I found that Danes are very good at laughing and very enthusiastic about this concept. Jan and many other laughter leaders are conducting seminars and workshops in many organisations, corporations and social groups.

Laughter Clubs in Norway
(A Report by Franciska Munck)

In April 1999 I was sitting on an airplane on my way to Zürich, Switzerland, reading the flight magazine. Suddenly I saw a picture of thousands of laughing people from India. I read the article with huge interest, and got a strong feeling that I should contact the man behind the laughter. Back in Norway I sent Dr. Kataria an e-mail asking if we could meet. I got a welcoming mail back and two weeks later I arrived in Mumbai. It was a very special and positive meeting with the Laughter Club members, the Indian culture, and not least, two exceptionally open and friendly people, Dr. Kataria and his wife Madhuri. This gave me memories for a lifetime and a whole new way of using laughter. In Norway we use laughter exercises alone or combine them with courses in motivation, for all types of companies, organizations etc.

Today we have more than 150 certified laughter leaders all over the country, who use laughter exercises in various ways. In addition to the laughter sessions we are conducting for groups, we have two big Laughter Clubs in Oslo and some smaller ones around the country. We have had laughter sessions for all kinds of groups. For business leaders in Norwegian oil companies, for children in kindergartens, schoolchildren, doctors and nurses, prisoners, disabled persons, people with hearing disabilities, religious people, athletes etc. We have had many big moments with laughter, but the one that I remember the most, must be the session we had in "Holmenkollen - Tasjansen" in Oslo. On Sunday the 25th of June 2000, we celebrated the first Norwegian Laughter Day by having a laughter session for 10,400 people. It was a big moment to go on stage in front of so many people, together with ten of the laughter leaders and make them all laugh. We made laughter contests, we did a big laughter wave, and to end it all we made a record attempt where we all laughed together.

Laughter is, as I see it, the pathway to something bigger. I see laughter as a great way to spread love around us. It is our opportunity to unite and heal the world. It is our opportunity to remove boundaries and come together in a peacefull and nonjudgemental way. I support Dr. Kataria in every way in his wish to create world peace through laughter. I am convinced that every single person we reach out to with laughter, joy and love is an important step to more peace in the world, and to more joy and happiness in all of us. This is only the beginning!

LAUGHTER MOVEMENT IN FRANCE

Many articles on Laughter Clubs appeared in newspapers and maganizes all over France and I used get many inquiries from the people who were interested in starting Laughter Clubs in France. In early 2001 Daniel Kiefer, a young businessman from Mulhouse, saw a documentary film on Laughter Clubs of India. He was inspired and joined me for a training workshop in Copenhagen. He started the first Laughter Club in France and organsied two workshop in May-June 2002. On 13th June a film on Laughter Clubs appeared on the most popular programme on national television called "Envoy Special". This created awareness about Laughter Clubs all over France. At present there are Laughter Clubs in Mulhouse run by Daniel Kiefer, a Laughter Club in Paris organised by Jocelyne Le Moan and a Laughter club in Frontignan, South France organised by Corinne Cosseron.

LAUGHTER MOVEMENT IN ITALY
(REPORT BY ROBERTA FIDORA FROM MILANO, ITALY)

The first time I met Madan was when he arrived in Milano (Italy) on a cold, foggy winter morning in October 2001. We had only communicated by e-mail and spoken on the phone once. Neither of us knew what to expect from each other. Obviously I knew everything about his laughter activity in India and throughout the world, but nothing about his personality. My husband and I invited him to stay with us for a week. It was an amazing experience. I organized an Indian dinner to meet the press, a public seminar attended by 200 people, meetings with multinational corporations, interviews with television and the 2-day "laughter seminar" with 40 participants. Italians welcomed this new therapeutical concept created by Madan, with a lot of enthusiasm. I too was enthusiastic! My asthma problems disappeared for a whole week and Madan also taught me not to be too stressed by work.

I remember when I first spoke about Madan to friends and corporation managers. Skepticism was the immediate emotion I saw in their eyes. "How can you laugh for no reason?" they would ask me "it sounds a bit stupid...".

By the way, Madan, came to Italy one month after the 11 September attack. I too was worried. More than once I asked myself if it was right to talk about laughter at such a sad and tragic time. When I saw Madan "at work", when I saw him comunicate with the public, when I heard him

Laughter meditation at Town Hall Square in Copenhagen, Denmark.

explaining the philosophy of laughter and the important mission he brought worlwide I understood I had done the right thing in inviting him to Italy. People understood it was not just a matter of laughing, the idea behind was much deeper and more important: peace and laughter.

During that week in October 2001, we started to put in place the basis for a laughter movement in Italy. I decided to start a Laughter Club in Milano: we meet once a month and we are 25/30 people. We divide all the expenses (renting the place) and after each meeting we all eat together. Each of us brings food and drinks. There are Laughter Clubs in Florence, Bolzano and Gubbio (near Rome). On the island of Sicily, the psychologist Franco Scirpo helps mentally disabled children with Madan's laughter therapy.

Laughter Clubs in Australia
(Report compiled by Shirley Hicks from Sydney)

Laughter Clubs Australasia commenced in the late 1990s, due to the dedication of the Adelaide-based Magician and Public Speaker, Peter Salerno.

Peter was instrumental in highlighting the health benefits of laughter, not only to other Australians, but he also carried the message overseas to Malaysia where he has assisted in the establishment of Laughter Clubs. Since Peter's early interest in the techniques developed in India and practiced by more than a thousand laughter club all over India, the Laughter Club concept has spread to other states in Australia. Laughter Clubs now operate in Queensland, New South Wales, Victoria and Western Australia.

There are now approximately 40 Laughter Clubs operating in Australia with new clubs coming on-line all the time. The Australian experience with the Laughter Club concept, whilst still in its infancy, bodes well for the future growth of Laughter Clubs throughout the Pacific region.

Media support for Laughter Clubs has been exceptional. Many of the Laughter Club leaders have been extensively involved in radio interviews, with Susan Welch, the Queensland co-ordinator utilising radio very effectively to educate the general public about the health benefits of laughter. Earlier this year, Radio National presented an excellent story covering the New South Wales-based Laughter Clubs. As quoted in this interview, participants were glowing with the results that they gained from regular laughter sessions. One particular participant, who has struggled with seriously poor lung health his entire life, quotes the Laughter Club as being the "most effective bronchodilator" that he has come across in all the years of treatment that he has received. Other participants say that they will never miss a Laughter Club session as it has provided them with not only a valuable boost to their health but also a community of like-minded, fun people with whom they can let their hair down and just laugh. In Adelaide, Peter maintains a regular radio spot and continues to educate the public about how they can become more spontaneous in their joy and laughter.

Laughter Clubs, as profiled on national television programs, such as *Body & Soul* and *Health Dimensions*, have increased general public awareness greatly. Most people when asked will say that they have heard of Laughter Clubs. Local community and health groups have warmly embraced the concept, with many leaders volunteering their time and expertise to bring the benefits of laughter to the widest cross section of people. Organisations such as Mission Australia, The Schizophrenia Fellowship, Cancer Support groups, women's health centres, high schools and technical colleges are all looking towards incorporating laughter into the programs that they offer their clients.

In conjunction with this growing acceptance for yogic laughter, our trans Tasman cousins in New Zealand are now waking up to the health benefits that laughter can provide. New Zealand based, Pat Armistead is also dedicated to spreading the concept of laughter yoga.

A REPORT BY SUSAN WELCH FROM BRISBANE

Laughter Clubs, which I describe as "the thread that is weaving society together, one stitch of laughter at a time", are also doing great work in Australia, and spreading quickly. Although my experience as a Laughter Yoga Instructor is relatively new, I believe that when you find your passion, combined with such valuable community service work, the universe rushes in to support you. In the first three months of running Laughter Clubs in Queensland, I have had thousands of people come through sessions and I have trained two dozen people to run clubs.

The public acceptance of Laughter Clubs here has been unequivocal, people know that these clubs are therapeutic and they accept them wholeheartedly as tools to improve their health and happiness, relationships with each other, and overall, to get society back together.

Although we are not as formalised as American Laughter Clubs, or as big as Indian Laughter Clubs, we are not short on enthusiasm! The New South Wales clubs, under the direction of Shirley Hicks, a naturopath, have been in existence longer than the Queensland and Victoria clubs. Peter Salerno, in South Australia, has done much previously with laughter, humour and motivational speaking, while Ian Hall is happily at the helm in Western Australia. Phillipa Challis, a keynote speaker, has overseen the formation of Victorian clubs, and all credit to her for doing so despite her health challenges! Phillipa really believes in the healing power of laughter.

We eagerly await the commencement of clubs in the Northern Territory, Tasmania and Australian Capital Territory. Regionally and rurally, my aim is to have Laughter Clubs available to all who want to access them. We are all well on the way to a more formalised association of Laughter Clubs in Australia, and remain connected in spirit by what we do and why we do it.

Physically, mentally and emotionally, laughter has done wonders for some of our previously seriously ill club members. Some of the testimonials I have heard have been real tear-jerkers. One of the women that attends Laughter Club sessions on the Gold Coast had a double lung replacement, and attributes her speedy recovery and health improvement to laughter and the positive outlook it gives people. A Redcliffe club woman had been seriously ill long term with chronic fatigue and depression. She described "using laughter and singing to get (herself) out of an oppressive hospitalisation through the out-door, not the morgue door". A Sydney testimonial came from a serious car accident victim, who was befriended by Laughter Club members, and whose rehabilitation was sped up considerably compared to her prognosis. The woman was uplifted by the compassion and positivity of the group, who would carry her to sessions regularly, until she finally had the strength to stand unaided. Just as amazing as the testimonials we have heard are the places laughter yoga can permeate. There seem to have been no doors unopened when laughter knocks.

I have started Laughter Clubs in City Councils, schools - with both students and teachers - in psychology practices, with diversional therapists, in aged care, with special needs people, in health retreats, and soon hopefully in corrective services and emergency services. I have seen laughter reunite people, improve work and play spaces and give participants hope and health. At a recent Laughter Club Leader meeting in June 2002, our Australian Laughter Club's mission statement was decided as:

"Laughter Clubs are a voluntary, community-based organisation committed to bringing the health and social benefits of yogic laughter to all members of the community. Through the formation of group laughing,

The Laughter Club of Mulhouse, France.

participants are supported to discover that happiness and laughter are states of mind and laughter can be an unconditional state of being, irrespective of the ups and downs of life.''

We look forward to a united future through laughter, and the imminent approach of laughter's acceptance as "the best medicine", at all levels.

As Doctor Jane Yip, Australia's leading research psychologist into laughter, recently remarked: "This is the beginning of a very promising peaceful social initiative with the potential to unite the world regardless of class, gender, race, political and religious affiliations because we all laugh in the same way. Scientifically speaking we may be scratching the surface of a new field: social psychological intervention to health and group effectiveness - a much needed area in this stressful world. It is my dream that in the not too distant future, Laughter Yoga can find a place in health benefits schemes, to help lessen the burden of the public's dependency on pharmacetucials to cope with depression, pain and stress. We also look forward to finding suitable sponsors to fund the valuable work that many of us continue to do on a voluntary basis.''

Laughter Clubs In Malaysia
(A report by Mahes Karuppiah)

I have been practicing laughter therapy since I got infected by it in Mumbai in 1999 when I lived with Dr Kataria's family and learned the ropes from the guru himself. I would like to see Malaysians laughing their way to well-being and I have made possible different approaches to laughter. Being a disciple of the Katarian school of thought (power of laughter) and an Universal Tao Teacher (magic of smiles), I know I will make the difference. Laughter activates and animates the whole human anatomy. It is not only a tool for communication, it is also a vehicle to release pent-up stress of the mind and body. Laughter releases "energies" that recreate, reactivate and re-empower the human spirit.

I am part of a Paradigm Shift, playing a part in shaking up current thinking and practices in a big way, making people look into innate qualities like laugher, smiles, love, joy, happiness and pure play. I have not only changed my life but am instrumental in rekindling a flame deep within people I come in contact with.

The "New Age" philosophy, a marriage of Eastern and Western approaches of holism, a systemic awareness of the interrelatedness of all things, is shaking up the whole world and I am playing a part in Malaysia. Transpersonal psychology incorporates the spiritual aspects, combining Eastern philosophy with Western psychological techniques.

Laughter Conference In Kaula Lampur, Malaysia

For the first time an educational institution, the University of Malaya invited Dr. Kataria and his wife to attend the first-ever Laughter Conference in Malaysia on 3rd August 2002. It was attended by more than 800 University students and members of the general public. Dr. Madan Kataria was the keynote speaker who spoke about the worldwide laughter movement and benefits of laughter.

Laughter In Dubai (A Report By Ram Ganglani)

I am based in Dubai, U.A.E., and I first heard about the Laughter Clubs about five years ago, while spending my holidays in Mumbai stay-

Dr. Kataria leading a laughter session with a group of executives in Dubai.

ing with my cousin in Bandra. She had heard a lot about the laughter sessions held at Jogger's Park. Knowing about my interest in self-development books and seminars etc., she thought this could fall within my line of interest. She pushed me to take her along for the session, as she herself had not taken the initiative to check it out for herself.

On arrival at the venue, I was very hesitant to participate in the group, as it all looked silly and foolish to me. But after a few moments, when I saw they were having fun and enjoying it, we thought, "Why not join them?" After all we will be part of the group, doing what they are doing, so there should be no reason to feel embarrassed. As we slipped into the group, we started following the directions of the leader and it all seemed so easy, we felt good, we felt relaxed and were happy that we were there. It appeared the participants were all regular at the session as each one was very familiar with the whole routine. We were clearly identified as new faces. So, just before the session ended, we were asked to come forward to introduce ourselves as they wished to welcome new participants with a special hearty laughter.

When I came back to Dubai, I started mentioning the laughter concept to my friends and business contacts and realized that many people had heard about the Laughter Clubs all over India and were excited about the thought of starting something on those lines over here. I got in touch with Dr. Kataria and also checked out his website. I soon learnt that one could also consider running in-house laughter workshops for the corporate sector, using laughter as one way to reduce stress and increase productivity at the workplace. I then felt it would be viable to invite Dr Kataria through our company, Right Selection, to run a few sessions for corporate houses, whereby they would partially sponsor his visit. We also planned to run a few public sessions which we could sponsor.

Fortunately, at about that time, my son Gautam who also plans our seminars and workshops was in Mumbai on holiday. I encouraged him to meet Dr Kataria personally to finalise his visit and gather all the details necessary for us to make our preparations.

The final result was that in November 2000 Dr. and Mrs. Kataria landed in Dubai for a week-long trip. Thus materialized Dr. Kataria's first visit to Dubai along with his laughing partner, his wife Madhuri, in November 1999. During the course of 7 days, we had about 10 laughter sessions at different venues. There were laughter sessions for the corporate sector, for yoga groups, for children with special needs and in general for the public who were serious about learning the laughter concept.

It was great fun, laughing in large groups. At the end of it all, we all felt very light, totally de-stressed and on a high as if we were in a different world. The following year Dr. Kataria visited Dubai once again to officially launch the "Emirates Laughter Group" to encourage us to run laughter sessions on a regular basis. Due to the pattern of life here and the long working hours, for practical purposes we have only been able to organise a laughter session once every month, which is stretched to a complete evening program to include fun and games in the second part of the session following by dinner and socializing. However, there are other groups like the yoga groups in Bur Dubai, Deira and Sharjah who have incorporated a brief laughter session in their daily exercises as they conclude their yoga session every day.

The Laughter Club of Singapore.

LAUGHTER CLUBS IN SINGAPORE

Singapore was the first country to send me an invitation which was sponsored by a Government department. The Lifeskills & Lifestyle Division of the People's Association invited me to hold a full-day workshop to train a group of laughter leaders in the year 2000. Four community Laughter Centres were established in 2001. Thomas Peh Chee Kin organised the Laughter Clubs and two Laughter Clubs are very popular in Singapore. One, run by Zareena Bana, is the East Coast - Joo Chiat Laughter Club and the second run by Gellene Lim (Miss), is the Northeast - Tampines GRC Laughter Club. In November 2001, the Ministry of Manpower organised the Singapore Learning Festival where more than 1000 business people participated and I was invited to speak on Community Learning through Laughter. The idea was appreciated as a possible breakthrough in stress management in the corporate world.

LAUGHTER CLUBS IN THE UK

The first international television news channel to cover the Laughter Club news was BBC World and numerous articles appeared in magazines and newspapers about the new concept of Laughter Clubs. But, it took a long time before I could establish the first Laughter Club in the UK. I trained several laughter leaders in Copenhagen and Zurich who were from the UK, but it was Paul Maguire from Birmingham who took the initiative to establish the first Laughter Clubs in Solihull, Birmingham. I did a laughter workshop in Birmingham followed by a very successful public seminar at Brinxton hall in London. Julie Whitehead, a yoga teacher from London successfully started the first Laughter Club in London. It seems that the Laughter Club idea has finally taken off in the UK, thanks to Paul Maguire, Julie Whitehead and Laura.

Laugh Like a Spanish Dancer

CHAPTER - 10

The Essential Link Between Yoga and Laughter

What does a simple emotion like laughter and an universally acclaimed form of exercise such as yoga have in common? Yoga has always been distinguished as a classic system of ancient Indian philosophy because of the marvels of bodily control instilled by its practice. Yoga produces an unique physiological balance in the human body by connecting body, mind and spirit. Laughter, on the other hand, is a cognitive, affective and behavioural response familiar to every one of us. Let us try to find similarities between the two.

The word "Yoga" arises from the Sanskrit root 'Yuj' which means to get hold of, integrate, harmonize. It means getting hold of our lives, integrating all aspects of life, harmonizing our bodies with our minds, spirits and society. When I first thought about the idea of Laughter Clubs, it was only to have fun and laughter. I didn't have yoga in my mind at all. Inspite of initial ridicule by people, I pursued the idea till most of the members in public parks accepted it as an enjoyable exercise. When jokes didn't work, we learnt to laugh without them. I thought of how to make all the members practice these laughter sessions everyday for 10-15 minutes because everybody felt nice after their morning guffaws. Morning walkers are obviously health-conscious people and they would want to do it religiously.

I have been a student of yoga and used to give health talks at one of the popular Yoga institutes in Mumbai. I thought, why not connect laughter exercise with yoga? For a few days I kept thinking about different aspects of yoga and how they could be connected to laughter. I went through a couple of books on yoga and gained an insight – Why not deliberately structure all the laughter exercises on yoga?

DEEP BREATHING

Since the act of laughter depends upon our breathing apparatus, the lungs and respiratory muscles, I thought of starting each session with (*Pranayama*) deep breathing, which is an important part of yoga. Deep breathing has a calming effect on the mind and provides more oxygen to body tissues. Secondly, I wanted to give some pauses in-between the

Most laughter yoga exercises are done with arms raised upwards.

bouts of laughter and I thought : Why not intersperse the different types of laughter with deep breathing? This will definitely increase the vital capacity of the lungs and hence their capacity to laugh. Later on, I realized that deep breathing is one of the most important parts of laughter exercises. In the normal course, the common man has no patience to do yogic deep breathing. We made it an integral part of a laughter session and thus it became a ritual.

RAISING THE ARMS UP IN THE SKY

Normally, yogic deep breathing is done slowly and rhythmically with concentration and perhaps visualization. But this was not possible in a group where most people were standing. To give a rhythm and slow tempo I told my fellow participants to raise both their arms up towards the sky, and at the same time breath in slowly and deeply. After inspiration they were asked to hold the breath and stretch the arms for 4 seconds and then breathe out slowly through the mouth, as if whistling silently, while bringing the arms down. The idea of breathing out through the mouth was to prolong the expiration, as in a variety of *Pranayama,* the expiration time is double the time of inspiration. Scientifically speaking, even when one exhales completely, there is some amount of air left in the lungs, called residual air. This residual volume is more in those suffering from chronic bronchitis and asthma. There are more chances of bacterial infection and less exchange of oxygen if the residual volume is more. Prolonged expiration as in *Pranayama* and some dynamic breathing exercises help to remove the residual air, which contains more carbon dioxide, and replace it with fresh air which contains more oxygen. This is how deep breathing and laughter help to increase the net supply of oxygen to the body for better functioning.

Ho-Ho, Ha-Ha Exercise

If one observes the process of laughter carefully, one will see that during the act of laughter there is a rhythmic movement of the diaphragm (the major respiratory muscle which separates the thoracic cavity from the abdominal cavity), abdominal muscles and intercostal muscles (between the ribs) which helps to expel the air from the lungs in rhythmic jerks which produces rhythmic vibrations from the vocal cords. Also, there is contraction of the throat, palate muscles and facial muscles. There are some dynamic yogic exercises called *Kapalbhati, Swash Shuddi* (cleaning of respiratory passages in forceful jerks of breathing) and *Bhastarika,* which involve similar rhythmic contraction of all the groups of muscles involved in laughter.

In my search for a method of how to laugh without any reason, when they were told to force themselves to laugh, many people found it difficult to laugh. Therefore, I introduced a warm-up exercise of laughter called Ho-Ho Ha-Ha. People would open their mouth and chant in unison this Ho-Ho Ha-Ha. Doing so helped remove inhibitions and there was a sense of participation by the members. The whole atmosphere got charged with laughter and many people would get stimulated and start smiling and giggling.

This Ho-Ho Ha-Ha exercise has some similarity with *Kapalbhati,* and *Swash Shuddi* (respiratory passage cleaning with jerky movements of the abdominal muscles). Later this Ho-Ho Ha-Ha exercise was supplemented with rhythmic clapping of the hands, which gave good stimulation to the acupressure points in the hand. The Ho-Ho Ha-Ha exercise, along with clapping, is done at least 3-5 times at the end of each bout of laughter.

DEEP BREATHING WITH ARM STRETCHING

While taking a deep breath in between the laughter techniques, the arms are stretched, which is similar to a yogic exercise known as *Talasana*. In addition, there are neck and shoulder exercises, designed to exercise the muscles around the neck and shoulders which are tight because of the stress and strain of modern life.

LION LAUGHTER

Another type of laughter that is practised exclusively in Laughter Clubs, which is similar to *"Simha Mudra"* of yoga, is Lion laughter. Here, a person is supposed to laugh while fully extruding the tongue, keeping the eyes wide open and posing the hands like the paws of a lion. This is a direct adoption of the yogic lion pose. This posture has proved to be good exercise for facial muscles and beneficial for throat ailments. According to yoga experts, this also stimulates the thyroid gland. Often such kinds of laughter are embarrassing, especially for women in a social gathering. But the participants of Laughter Clubs gradually get over such inhibitions and hence this exercise provides its full benefits.

CHAPTER - 11

Scientific Rational of Yoga & Laughter

All the organs of the body are made up of tissues. To keep these tissues in perfect health and organic vigour, there should be a constant supply of nourishment like proteins, carbohydrates, fats, salts, minerals and vitamins. These are derived from one's food and drink. Their supply depends upon the quality of food one eats and the power of digestion and absorption of the digestive system. To reach the nutrients all over the body, one's circulatory systems should be efficient. Therefore, the digestive and circulatory systems should be kept in good order for optimum health. Finally, when the nutrients reach all the tissues of the body, oxygen is required for their metabolism. To get a better oxygen supply our respiratory systems must be in perfect order.

British actor John Cleese with Madhuri Kataria after a laughter session in a factory in Mumbai.

Toning up the Digestive System

According to principles of yoga, health and vigour of the body depend upon the quality and quantity of food. A lot of emphasis is given to selecting the right food. Since Laughter Club meetings are regular, a lot of awareness is being created about healthful food among the members. Eating of raw fruits, salads, vegetables and sprouts is being actively promoted in Laughter Clubs. Every morning it is a practice among many Laughter Club members to bring sprouts of various lentils. Sprouts are an excellent food containing large quantities of vitamins and are considered very healthful. Along with sprouts you will see cloves of raw garlic and basil leaves (a sacred Indian herb) kept at the venues of Laughter Clubs. Since Laughter Club members meet everyday, through the network, members receive information on various aspects of healthy eating. We are proposing to strengthen this network and constitute a panel of experts through the central body, the Laughter Club International. In a group, people get motivated to develop good eating habits.

Once you eat the right food, your digestive system should be in perfect order to get most of the nutrients from the food. All the principle organs of digestion like the stomach, intestines, liver and pancreas are situated in the abdominal cavity, supported by strong muscles from all sides. Nature has provided a gentle massage to all the digestive organs by the movement of the abdominal muscles and diaphragm twenty-four hours a day during normal respiration. During inspiration the diaphragm pushes the abdominal organs downwards and forwards and at the same time relaxes the abdominal wall muscles. During exhalation, the abdominal muscles are contracted and they push all the organs of the abdominal cavity inwards and upwards. Thus, nature has provided an automatic and gentle massage to the digestive organs 16-20 times a minute (normal respiration rate).

But, if the abdominal muscles are weak and the muscles of the diaphragm are not exercised regularly they cannot provide an effective massage. Today, due to a sedentary life style and obesity, abdominal muscles lose their tone, and this leads to excessive fat deposits on the abdominal wall. As a result, the abdominal organs get displaced from their normal places and their blood supply also gets affected. This can result in dyspepsia and a variety of digestion problems. To ensure perfect health of the digestive system, the abdominal muscles should be strong and elastic. There are many yogic poses which make them strong and elastic and give an excellent internal massage to the internal organs. For optimal performance, muscles should be contracted and stretched. Yoga *asanas* like *Bhunjagasana, Salabhasana* and *Dhanurasana* are some of the finest stretching excercises for the abdominal muscles. *Yoga-Mudra* and *Halasana* help to contract abdominal muscles.*Vakrasana* and *Ardha-Matsyendrasana* are excellent for side abdominal muscles.

There are two important yogic excercises *Uddiyana* and *Nauli* for internal massage: In *Uddiyana*, there is a vertical massage to the abdominal organs. A wave of contraction travels up and down in the abdominal muscle. Similarly, in *Nauli,* contractions travel from one side to the other, giving a lateral massage to the abdominal viscera. I admit that no other

A laughter workshop in the forest near Zurich, Switzerland.

excercises of abdominal muscles can match the perfect yogic excercise to build the strength of abdominal muscles and give an internal massage.

In Laughter Clubs we have different varieties of belly laughs which can excercise all the abdominal muscles and the diaphragm simultaneously. In between the laughter, there are stretching excercises for abdominal muscles by raising the arms, taking a deep breath. Scientists have called laughter 'internal jogging' or a 'Magic Finger' which goes right inside your tummy and gives an excellent massage to your internal organs. Regular laughter excercise not only strengthens the abdominal muscles and gives a constant massage, but also holds the abdominal organs in their proper places to ensure proper digestion and absorption. I agree, laughter excercises are no match for standard yogic *asanas*, but they can be done regularly to give excellent results at no cost.

FOR A STRONG CIRCULATORY SYSTEM

Once the food is digested properly and absorbed, the nutrients must reach each and every part of the body and the circulatory system is the transport system. All the nourishment is absorbed into the blood, proc-essed a bit in the liver and passed on to the central pumping system, the heart, to be pushed throughout the body through a network of blood vessels.

Similarly, the blood, after supplying the nutrients and collecting the wastes of metabolism should return to the heart and lungs for purifica-tion. The most important organ of circulation is the heart. By rythmic contraction and relaxation of the diaphragm and intercostal muscles, the resulting expansion and contraction of the lungs provide a good massage to the heart muscles. A constant change in intra-thoracic pressure while laughing helps to draw in venous blood returning from all the major venacavas of the upper and lower body. In a good bout of laughter, there is dilation of blood vessels all over the body giving a flushed apperance and feeling of warmth. Pulse rate and blood pressure rise as the circula-tion gets stimulated, before they settle down even below the original levels ten minutes after the cessation of Laughter Therapy. In a nutshell, laughter helps to tone up the circulatory system of the body.

FOR A STRONG RESPIRATORY SYSTEM

Once all the elements of nourishment are carried to the tissues, the most important element which forms a part of many enzyme systems of me-tabolism is oxygen. The principle organs of respiration are the lungs. For effective supply of oxygen, so that the full breathing capacity of lungs may be utilised, the respiratory passages should be clear and muscles of respiration should be strong.

Yoga lays more emphasis on breathing excercises because they help to improve oxygen supply for optimal function. The life force energy *prana*, enters our body through breathing. Therefore, breathing is the most important part of health building at the physical level, as it supplies oxy-gen. At the mental level it helps to calm down the mind and at the spir-itual level the life force energy can be upgraded through various types of breathing excercise *(Pranayams)*. I deliberately incorporated deep breath-ing excercises to provide a break in between two kinds of laughter. Nor-

A laughter session at Kalmar University in Sweden.

mally, in one's general routine, nobody remembers deep breathing, but in a Laughter Club one becomes habituated to deep breathing as it is done at least 10-15 times during each laughter session.

Normally, a person at rest breathes 16-18 times a minute. During daily tasks it goes up to 25-30 times a minute. During heavy excercise and intense emotional pressure, breathing can go up to 30-40 times a minute. Individuals suffering from chronic bronchitis, bronchial asthma or cardiac failure have higher respiratory rates. During the stress and strain of daily life, breathing rates go up and become shallow. As a few lung cells, due to lack of deep breathing, cease to participate in respiration, they have a tendency to collapse and become non-functional. The lung capacity (vital capacity) goes down and as a result the person feels breathless after a little exertion. Regular deep breathing, as practised in Laughter Clubs, keeps the lungs at their full breathing capacity and also helps in emotional calming down. If one wants to achieve higher spiritual levels one's breathing channel should be in perfect order.

Residual Volume

After the inspiration, when the air is exhaled, some amount of air is left within the lungs. That is known as residual air. This air contains more carbon dioxide and can only be removed by forced exhalation, or in a prolonged bout of laughter. There is a type of *Pranayam*, a breathing exercise where expiration is more prolonged than inspiration with the idea of removing as much air from the lungs as possible. In our laughter sessions, participants are advised to inhale through the nose and exhale through the mouth by making pursing gestures to prolong the expiration, so that the residual volume is replaced by fresh air, which contains more oxygen. Similarly, all the bouts of laughter are like prolonged exhalations with brief periods of inspiration. After 30-45 seconds of laughter, the laughter group is asked to relax and take two long deep brealths. This increases the net supply of oxygen to the body.

Clearing Respiratory Passages

Laughter sessions, along with deep breathing, are like chest physiotherapy for those who are smokers and have problems of bronchitis and respiratory airway obstruction. The Ho-Ho Ha-Ha exercise is akin to yogic *kriya* like *kapalphati, shwashuddi* and *bhastarika*, where exhalation is done in jerks with force. Many people feel that after a laughter session they keep bringing out some mucous during the day, which makes their breathing clear. Laughter also increases the local resistance in the throat and they thereby get fewer colds and attacks of tonsillitis. Various breathing excercises, along with Lion Laughter, help to keep their respiratory passages more healthy.

Effective Removal of Waste Products

Another condition which is important for maintaining health of the tissues is the effective removal of waste products from the body. Carbon dioxide is a by-product of metabolism and gets cleared from the system by deep breathing and a variety of stimulated laughter. The massage to the digestive tract provided by laughter exercises helps to maintain good bowel movements. Good tone of abdominal muscles also prevents constipation by promoting proper evacuation and bowel movements.

CHAPTER - 12

Is the Laughter in Laughter Clubs Real?

As I have stated elsewhere, to start with we took the help of jokes and humourous ancedotes to make people laugh, but the major hurdle to this endeavour was that there was not a large enough stock of good jokes. Besides, not everyone found all the jokes funny and most of them were targeted at some community or gender. This used to hurt the sentiments of one or the other. All this was, indeed, disappointing. Some went to the extent of suggesting that the idea of a Laughter Club or group laughter may be given up completely. After some soul searching, it became clear to me that if people have to laugh everyday, the idea of someone making them laugh would not be workable. That meant laughter had to be self-induced and for no reason except to derive its many benefits. When I put this idea before the group, the reaction was that of total disbelief. They could not comprehend that something that they had never seen happening could be possible. I was of the view that, in a group, not all laugh for the same reason. Some laughed because others were laughing. This we all witness in a cinema hall. When the whole hall roars with laughter, it is not because all have understood the joke.

After some explanation and pursuasion, the group agreed to give the idea of self induced laughter, laughter for no reason, a try and never regretted it. They were pleasantly surprised to see the good results that were turning out, gradually. Psychologists say that the human mind tends, initially, to resist any change even if it is for the better. Similarly, I think, anything new, particularly an idea such as that of laughing for no reason, draws cynicism. Many people, mostly from outside the group, expressed the opinion that laughter at the Laughter Clubs is artificial as compared to laughter arising from jokes etc., which they called natural. This artificial laughter they said, cannot possibly have any benefit. Since some people seem to be very struck with this thought, I propose to deal with it, at a little length, to put the matter into a proper perspective.

God has given mankind the capacity to laugh which he has not given to any other species. This capacity is inborn as even a newly born baby is able to laugh. What is, therefore, natural is this capacity to laugh and not any kind of laugher. Had this natural capacity to laugh not been given to us by God, probably no laughter of any kind whatsoever would exist.

DIFFERENCE BETWEEN THE TWO LAUGHTERS

Though the laughter resulting from a joke etc. and the laughter at the Laughter Clubs are not identical, if we look at them a little more closely, we find that there are more similarities between the two than differences. The difference is in the initial stage of providing a stimulus and triggering off laugher. In one case, a stimulus is provided and laughter is triggered, not by nature, but by something done by a person other than the laugher; in the other, it is by the laugher himself. Being convinced of the many benefits of laughter, a member of a Laughter Club goes there to derive those benefits. With that stimulus and motivation, triggering of laughter is not at all difficult. The reason is simple.

114

A laughter session in progress at Perth, Australia.

Mr. Paul Ekman and Mr. Robert Levenson, psychologists from the Univerity of California, have come to the conclusion that the advice, "Put on a happy face" may actually be beneficial. Their research has shown that facial expressions are not only reactions to emotional states but can provoke these states as well. The latter is what happens at Laughter Clubs.

After the efforts to trigger laughter, in one case made by another person and by the laugher himself in the other, the resulting laughter, in both cases, is triggered within and also comes from within the laugher. There is nothing to show that the source of laughter in the two cases is different. Dealing with the question of source of laughter, Dr. Robert Holden, who conducts laughter clinics in UK and has written the well known book "Laughter - the Best Medicine" says in that book: "The answer is elusive. Even if we could ask the Gods where laughter comes from, they would probably just laugh."

Recently at Laughter Clubs we have developed a number of playful laughter techniques which help us to convert our self-induced laughter exercises into real laughter. Moreover, in laughter meditation, real and genuine laughter springs like a fountain without any reason. This meditative laughter is much more spontaneous and far deeper than any laughter which arises from humor or a joke.

QUALITY OF LAUGHTER

At times, it is contended that the quality of laughter in the two cases is different, and one is more pleasurable than the other. This is also only an impression, and, of course, a wrong one. The source of laughter in all cases being the same, what I think is meant by quality, is the intensity of laughter. That, as also the pleasure drawn, cannot possibly depend on who or what triggers the laughter but, rather the reaction, i.e. how hearty the laughter is, whatever may be the type of laughter. The above is evidenced by the fact that all persons who hear a joke are not equally amused by it, and therefore, do not laugh with the same intensity. Some laugh heartily, others just smile and some are totally unmoved as they find the joke not at all funny. It is also true that some members of a Laughter Club laugh more heartily than others. That difference could be due to mood, level of commitment and degree of playfulness.

The pleasure and the benefits a person derives from laughter do not depend on the name of the laughter but on the extent to which he enjoys it. Therefore, if the thought of the laughter at the Laughter Clubs being artificial is withholding any one from becoming a Laughter Club member and deriving the benefits of laughter, my request to him is, please leave that doubt aside and walk up to the nearest Laughter Club without any further delay. You will not regret it. Even if you do not enjoy the experience or do not enjoy it much, as you will find from what is stated below, enjoyment will come, and till that happens, there will still be benefits, because scientists have found that even false laughter has benefits.

Research by Mr. Paul Ekman and Mr. Robert Levenson has shown that motions create emotions and emotions create motions. Even if you act like a happy man, over a period of time you become one. For a person to act happy is a little difficult (not impossible), but it becomes far easier to act out happiness in a group. This is exactly what happens in our Laughter

116

Clubs. We all are acting happy and the chemistry is changing to happiness according to Dr. Dale Anderson (from Minnesota, USA), who visited our clubs and found a lot of sense in the laughter at the Laughter Clubs. In fact, we acquired one slogan from him which is getting popular in Laughter Clubs which is, FAKE IT, FAKE IT... till you MAKE IT. Act chemistry, act chemistry and the chemistry becomes real. Thank you, Dr. Dale for a beautiful thought.

The Duchenne Smile

Although Norman Cousin's book "Anatomy of an Illness" on curing oneself with laughter was a layman's view point, scientific research too shows that smiles and laughter actually trigger pleasure centers in the brain, even if artificially induced. Dr. Paul Ekman has opined that we don't yet know what specific parts of the brain are involved in each emotion but we are gathering fundamental knowledge and showing that there is a brain pathway that allows you to generate your own emotions. Dr. Ekman has identified 18 different kinds of smiles, each of which uses slightly different muscles or groups of muscles. He found that a bored smile, a cynical smile, or smiling at someone's humiliation will do nothing to raise your spirits.

There is only one smile which activates the brain center for happiness and that is the 'Duchenne Smile', named after Guillaume Benjamin Amad Duchenne, a French neurologist who experimented with and studied the muscles of the face when engaged in smiling. He discovered that when lips part and turn up, the eyes crinkle up showing crows feet and the upper lip droops slightly, then there is heightened activity in the left anterior region of the cortex of the brain, which is the center for happy emotions. Even an induced smile can turn your gloominess into an upbeat mood.

Here I would like to quote the work of Dr. Dale Anderson, M.D. of the ACT NOW project based in Minnesota, USA. He has a beautiful exercise in his workshops, where he tells all the participants to hold a pen between their teeth and write a few words on a piece of paper. Because the facial expressions of holding a pen between the teeth resemble a smile or a wide grin, it produces happy chemicals in the brain and the mood changes. Similarly, when the same exercise is performed by holding the pen between the lips the facial expression resemble that of sadness, one feels low after some time.

BALAMCHALANA

There is a *Kriya* in the science of Yoga known as *Balamchalana*, in which one lies on the floor and begins to roll about and laugh for no reason. Another example of artificially induced laughter which turns into the real thing with practice.

Dr. Col. K.L. Chopra, father of world famous Dr. Deepak Chopra, writes in his book, *Life in Your Hands* about the yogic practice of intentional group laughter which was rarely seen before Laughter Clubs came into existence. I used to hear about isolated groups and some individuals who laughed loudly for a few minutes. This artificially induced laughter, according to psychotherapist Annnette Goodheart, is interpreted by the body as real and as a result, the brain induces a flow of happy molecules, which flood trillions of cells all over the body stabilising the hormonal system and enhancing immunity. Instead of isolated laughter practice, here the Laughter Clubs' different kinds of stimulated group laughter based on yoga are spreading all over the world.

VALUE ADDITIONS ALONG WITH LAUGHTER

Even if you regard laughter as a mere exercise, it tones up your facial muscles. People do a number of exercises for all the muscles of the body but there are very few exercises designed for facial muscles. Voluntary laughter is an excellent exercise for your facial muscles, throat muscles, lungs and abdominal muscles. It brings a happy glow to your face and makes your eyes shine with a thin film of tears which are squeezed from the lacrimal sacs during the act of laughter. Deep breathing is an integral part of Laughter Clubs. According to the science of yoga, life energy (*prana*) flows through the breath. By controlled and deep breathing we can enhance our own well-being. With the 20-25 minute package offered by the Laughter Club, you will carry home the healthy habit of deep breathing at least 10-20 times a day. This helps to increase the lung capacity, thus enhancing oxygen supply to the body.

Jan Thygesen Poulsen leads a laughter session at Copenhagen, Denmark.

One set of stretching exercises relaxes the muscles of the neck and shoulders, which become painful due to the stress and strain of modern life. According to yoga, the neck is like a bridge between the brain and the rest of the body. All the important nerves, spinal cord and blood vessels pass through the neck. Neck, shoulder and back muscles need to be in proper tone to maintain the free movement of the neck. Along with laughter, we do a lot of rhythmic clapping with outstretched hands. This also adds to well-being by stimulating acupressure points on the palms.

If you are not able to generate natural laughter, the simple chanting of Ho Ho Ha Ha will help to tone up your abdominal muscles. It gives an excellent internal massage to the digestive tract and enhances blood supply to important internal organs like the liver, spleen, pancreas, kidneys and adrenal glands.

You get an opportunity to meet with like-minded people, go for outings, celebrate birthdays, attend health seminars and workshops and participate in national and international events focussed on laughter and happiness. You will also establish contact with laughter lovers all over the world and may get an opportunity to visit other cities and countries on behalf of Laughter Clubs.

Talking about enjoying laughter at the Laughter Clubs, meet Mr. P.T. Hinduja (75 years young), winner of the 'Best Laughing Man' competition twice, once in 1996 among the members of the various Laughter Clubs of Mumbai and again, in September 1998, at the All India Laughter Convention held in Goa. He was declared the winner, because both times the judges found him to be enjoying his laughter the most. Someone asked him "How do you manage to enjoy your laughter? He replied. "When I found that I was not enjoying the laughter very much, a little introspection told me that it was I, my own self, who was preventing me from enjoying it, no one else. I then decided that I am going to enjoy my laughter at the Laughter Club to the maximum extent possible and thus derive the maximum benefits.'' That determination and a little action did the trick and put the principle "motions create emotions as much as emotions create motions" into action.

Laugh Like a Goth

CHAPTER - 13

The Difference Between Laughter Clubs and Humour Activities

What is the difference between laughter and humour? This is the most common question people ask me in my seminars and workshops all over the world. Let me make a statement that though we do laugh without using humourous activities, we are helping people to develop their sense of humour through laughter. Laughter and humour run in unity; they can not be separated. Humour is more subtle and it is the awareness and ability of a person to see something funny or express something in a funny way. Laughter is one of the expressions of humour. Laughter and humour have a cause and effect relationship. Humour is the cause and the effect is laughter, which brings physiological and biochemical changes in the body. But in Laughter Clubs we are do not use any type of humour as a cause, we use laughter as a cause which helps people to do away with their inhibitions and shyness and become more open and start seeing what's funny in life. In other words, laughter is helping our club members to develop a sense of humour. In Laughter Clubs we laugh without using any humourous activities to stimulate laughter. We laugh in a group at absolutely nothing, but that does not mean that there is no reason at all for group laughing. Laughing in a group at nothing itself makes the idea so absurd that it makes us laugh. Secondly, we are using the infectious and contagious nature of laughter as a reason for our stimulated laughter.

Why we are not using humour as a cause to stimulate laughter is because humour is a very mental and intelligent phenomenon and as perceived by the common man there are very few people who claim to have a good sense of humour. Therefore, they believe that they can't laugh much because they don't have a sense of humour. Thus, a Laughter Club is a place for the majority of people to bring more laughter to their lives without bothering much about their sense of humour. In fact, laughter itself helps them to open their perception and sense of humour. In Laughter Clubs, laughter is the cause and humour is the effect. It is like putting the cart before the horse and it works.

Our laughter president from USA, Steve Wilson has written his views about Laughter Clubs and humour. Here are some of the highlights:

What Makes the Methods of a Laughter Club Different From Other Humorous and Laughter-Filled Activities and Therapies?

❖ Laughter Clubs utilize a systematic activity approach that is based on a foundation of both ancient practices, such as yoga and meditation and modern medical science.

❖ Members of Laughter Clubs are engaged as active and interactive participants, not as a passive audience being entertained. It has been proved that people who actively participate in any humour and laughter activity get more benefits than those who passively receive humour and laugh. The source of laughter is within the body and one can generate laughter with conscious effort and committment anytime he or she wants to. Laughing at something is conditional laughter and is dependent upon the availability of the source.

Dr. Kataria at the World Health Day celebrations in Mumbai.

❖ Laughter Clubs promote laughter as a genuine form of exercise based on yoga stretches, along with rhythmic and dynamic breathing techniques based on yoga. Irrespective of the source of laughter, it brings about physiological and chemical changes which are conducive to good health.

❖ The therapeutic laughter program called the Laughter Club makes the natural and positive power of laughter a widely accessible health option, in long-term care for example. It is an activity that is emerging as recognized and valued by professional Activity Therapists and Recreation Therapists as well as counselors, nurses, social workers, teachers, chaplains, clowns and others. The therapeutic effects of laughter are due to a reduction in stress levels. Since most diseases today have some stress and psychological element, laughter has some therapeutic value against stress related disorders and psychological ailments. Let me emphasize once again that we are using laughter as a preventive medicine. Our slogan is "Laugh Before You Fall Sick". There is no substitute for conventional medical treatment but laughter can be added as complementary medicine along with popular medicine.

❖ Most often, the laughter activity takes place in a group that comes together with a common purpose and provides social support. Therefore, the method and viewpoint can be applied in communities as a form of social glue. The very reason why Laughter Clubs are spreading all over the world is that they bring people together and cultivate brotherhood and fellowship. These laughter activities are particularly relevant for bringing people from all over the world together because one does not have to use language as a base for laughter. This could be the real breakthrough for bringing the whole world together and I dream of a unified world as a 'Universal Laughing Family'.

❖ Since Laughter Clubs are group activities, they help people to inspire and motivate each other to keep working on their inhibitions and shyness till they find their sense of humour. Remember, laughter is not an individual phenomenon but it is a group activity and much easier to come by when practised in a group. The laughter group members act as a source of motivation and help each other to keep going. Otherwise, as in any other health building activity, there is an element of boredom and the chances of abandoning such activities are much higher.

❖ A Laughter Club's therapeutic model has a structure that can be learned; leaders can be trained. Leaders demonstrate, motivate, educate and inspire. Certified Laughter Leaders operate with ethical guidelines.

❖ If humour occurs in a Laughter Club session, it is a spontaneous occurrence within the group, not forced, expected or required. We are in the early stages of understanding what it is that people find funny during these specifically no-joke-telling therapeutic laughter sessions.

❖ Humour is personal and subjective; laughter is universal. When jokes are used to evoke laughter, many people don't get the joke, or don't like the joke. Using jokes runs the risk of being offensive or hurtful. Laughter Clubs operate on a value system that minimizes and eliminates this risk.

❖ Humour is difficult to define and "funniness" is almost impossible to measure. However, the physiological changes that accompany laughter are relatively easy to measure and the benefits can be observed and studied more readily.

- Unlike comedy routines, Laughter Clubs can meet as often as the group likes without becoming stale or boring. This is because thousands of people are involved, which continuously keeps adding to the creativity and keeps the laughter sessions alive.

- Because we have a common method and shared values, Laughter Club leaders and members can form a global network to share ideas and to give each other encouragement and inspiration. Through the network of leaders and members, the method will improve continuously. New exercises are always being invented and we are discovering necessary cultural adaptations too. The international clearinghouse function of www.worldlaughtertour.com has been invaluable in this regard.

- Laughter Clubs are open to everyone; nobody is excluded. Laughter Clubs are non-political, non-religious, non-exploitive and non-commercial. Let me clarify here that there is no individual membership fee to become a Laughter Club member anywhere in the world. However, there is an affiliation fee for a laughter group so that we can keep providing updates, innovations and scientific information. The laughter leader training programmes are chargeable. If there are some incidental charges involved in hiring the venue for the Laughter Club the cost has to be shared by the club members. The use of laughter activities in profit making corporations and business houses is chargeable to generate funds for promoting the laughter movement around the globe.

- The systematic therapeutic laughter methods are adaptable to all ages, backgrounds, and even adapt to various physical and mental (cognitive) limitations.

- Systematic therapeutic laughter methods address body, mind and spirit. We have a philosophy behind our laughter movement - 'Laugh and make others laugh', 'Laugh and have the spirit of laughter'. Through the Spirit of Laughter, participants in Laughter Clubs achieve a better balance of emotions, reduce the negative effects of stress, release harmful anger and judgementalism and find a path to world peace.

❖ Because there is a common method, philosophy and values, Laughter Clubs link members and enthusiasts all around the world. Laughter Clubs promote observances of World Laughter Day (the first Sunday in May).

❖ Laughter Clubs are not limited by language differences. Laughter has no accent.

❖ Laughter Clubs provide a sense of belonging and of being involved in a worthwhile cause.

Laugh Like a Roman Emperor

CHAPTER - 14

How Do You Convert Laughter Exercises into Genuine Giggles?

Iif you happen to see any laughter group forcing their laughter, without any fun and pleasure, don't frown. It still has benefits and remember that with all the benefits of acting happy are value additions like deep breathing and stretching exercises based on yoga. If you find that a particular group's quality of laughter is not very amusing, perhaps they might not have been trained properly. There are many ways we can transform stimulated laughter into intermittent spontaneity. Here are a few techniques: 1. Good eye contact 2. Theory of stupidity 3. Playfulness and fun 4. Childlike actions 5. Gibberish talk.

EYE CONTACT IS THE KEY

Want to see the magic? Select someone close to you and look into the eyes of that person. Start smiling slowly and then giggle a bit. You will see that the other person will start laughing without even knowing why

A laughter session in progress at Saibaba garden in Mumbai, India.

you laughed. It is because of the infectiousness of laughter and the absurdity of the situation. This is the most important factor we apply in Laughter Clubs to initiate laughter. Eye contact, effectively applied, is enough to generate laughter. People who are too shy to have eye contact lack self-confidence. Therefore, learning to have good eye contact during a laughter session will also enhance your self-confidence. This self-confidence will be projected into your personal life as well as in business. The spontaneity of laughter in Laughter Clubs will depend upon the effective use of eye contact with other members of the group.

THEORY OF STUPIDITY AND SILLINESS

People who really understand the philosophy of laughing without reason can laugh without any problem. But today, everyone needs to be convinced and wants a logical answer. If you find it hard to get into the spiritual depths of laughter, then think in the most simple way. This is known as the "Theory of Stupidity. At the outset, the very name "Laughter Club" is amusing to many people and makes them laugh silently in their hearts. The onlookers in public parks can't help laughing when they see a group of gigglers laughing for no reason. On the face of it, it is the absurdity or stupidity which makes then laugh. The idea of a Laughter Club makes then laugh. Laughter Club members laugh for the enlightenment and health benefits they get, but onlookers laugh at their stupidity. Whatever it is, the idea is ongoing and mind-tickling and sufficiently absurd-sounding to attract people. They then find plenty of reasons to become regular members. I have interviewed many people who swear by their health that the Laughter Club has changed their lives, but initially they thought that it was foolish and laughed at its stupidity.

This theory can even help one to laugh at poor and already heard jokes. Someone asked me, "How can I laugh at a joke which I have already heard?" I said, "Why not? Another reason for you to laugh it that you already know the joke which is being told to you by someone with great effort and you may start laughing in your mind even before the punch line is delivered." Believe me, I have laughed at many sick and poor jokes because of this theory of stupidity. This will happen only if you look into the person's face closely while he is telling a joke which you already know.

Another effective reason to laugh at a poor joke is that it is good for one's health if one laughs. A Laughter Club member can easily laugh at anything because he practices every day. Another possibility is, if you already know a joke don't worry. The style of relating it might be more amusing if you watch carefully. You may enjoy the joke in a better way than when you heard it earlier. While you are participating in a Laughter Club, if you happen to make eye contact with someone who is laughing for no reason and in a funny way, it becomes a reason for you to laugh. One member may think that other members are stupid!

Another application of this theory is that if you want to laugh alone looking into the mirror, try to imitate the laughter of some one you know, maybe a movie character, Say Ha Ha Ha Ha and continue this for some time. If you are not able to do proper immitation you will feel silly. The moment one begins to feel stupid or silly, a genuine laughing sensation springs up, which is a great feeling and can be enjoyed as long as one allows the feeling of stupidity to persist.

SILLINESS OPENS PERCEPTION

There is lot to learn from the silliness in Laughter Clubs. A person who can laugh at himself without caring about the people who are watching him, is a person who can make his laughter real. In the beginning when we decided to abandon jokes and laugh for no reason, some people found it difficult to come out of their shells. To remove inhibitions we tried child-like actions like swivelling the tongue, talking gibberish and dancing in a funny way. Silliness really opened the doors of perception. Being silly is the first step towards freedom and creativity. The word silly is derived from *sealy*, which means blessed, happy and joyful. We all have been silly during our childhood and played with endless possibilities of non-sense, absurdity and silliness. In fact, all great inventors were snubbed as silly to begin with and the rest is history. Silliness is the gateway for inventions and innovations. A serious person will never take a chance for he is always afraid of ridicule by others. He will hesitate to explore possibilities and will not always be ready for experimentation.

Lastly, silliness will help to develop egolessness in a person. A person who can laugh at himself will not have a bloated ego. The ego is the seat of many negative emotions like anger, jealousy and greed. We play silly games in Laughter Clubs and it is amazing to see creativity at its best when the members come up with funny ideas every now and then. Acting silly is one of the basic necessities of being a Laughter Club member. Once your inhibitions are removed, you will find yourself at your best.

PLAYFULNESS IN LAUGHTER CLUBS

There is a saying that we don't stop playing because we are old, but we grow old because we stop playing. Playfulness gives immense pleasure especially in a group. If you observe people playing games without stakes and gambling, you will always observe smiles and some laughter. Children laugh a lot while playing any game. Playfulness is restricted only to our school days. Play is abandoned as soon we enter college.

As adults, people become very serious and are sure that playing is only meant for children. And whenever adults play, they play to kill time or starting gambling along with the game and it is rarely accompanied by smiles or laughter, while children always play for fun. In Laughter Clubs we have devised different types of stimulated laughter with a lot of playfulness. Swinging laughter, one meter laughter and cocktail laughter, argument laughter, mobile phone laughter and milk-shake laughter are some of the examples. In Laughter Clubs we remind people over and again that no one is ever too old to play and that the spirit of play lives forever.

FUN GAMES IN LAUGHTER CLUBS

Keeping up with the playfulness we are developing many fun games. We play during picnics and also during our regular meetings. Many Laughter Clubs and thousands of members are engaged in creating new ideas and fun games which have tremendous potential to make people laugh. These fun games can make people laugh better than jokes. The most important thing is that the members actively participate and create laughter, rather than passively watch any humourous thing.

CHILD-LIKE ACTIONS IN LAUGHTER CLUBS

If you want to get rid of your dependence on jokes and still want to laugh, simply become child-like. In the initial stages of the genesis of Laughter Clubs when we found jokes could not make us laugh much, we forced ourselves to laugh in a group. But many people found it mechanical and used to become a bit bored with the activity. Laughing in a group provides a stimulus, while child-like behaviour by adults helps them to get over their inhibitions. We do lot of child-like actions in Laughter Clubs; like producing funny sounds by swivelling the tongue inside the mouth, tapping air-filled cheeks, laughing like a child and talking gibberish. We keep reminding our members about the importance of being like a child.

Robert Holden is his book "Laughter the Best Medicine" says: "Every child is born with abundant creative potential for laughter, fun, play, happiness and love. Any restraint on any of these has an adverse effect on the child's growth and development. Anyone who grows with the inner child will find health, harmony and happiness. Therefore, instead of growing out of the child, we should grow with the child.''

As adults, very few persons retain the excitement of a child. Poems have been written about the desire to get back to one's childhood days. This alone is not enough. Some additional action is necessary. Just as one cannot learn swimming without getting into the water, one can be child-like only by behaving like a child. In a given period of time every day we, all the Laughter Club members, try to revisit our childhoods and try to carry that carefree spirit over to daily life. Child-like activities can be done either with one's own children/grandchildren or in a group of adults at Laughter Clubs.

GIBBERISH GAME

Talking gibberish is one of the best methods to drain out stress. It has very good cathartic value. But in Laughter Clubs we use this as a tool to remove inhibitions and act like children so as to create laughter. Nowadays it is being extensively used as a warm-up exercise in Laughter Clubs to open up. In addition to gibberish talking, there are many humour activating techniques like gibberish singing, gibberish contests and whiff-piff talking which help the members to generate laughter.

CHAPTER - 15

Sensible Living: Paying Compliments - The Inner Laugh

Soon after Laughter Clubs started gaining momentum, the wife of a Laughter Club member telephoned me to complain that while her husband laughed heartily every morning in his Laughter Club, at home he continued to shout at the family members, the same as he did earlier. Then she asked: Should not Laughter Clubs be doing something to see that laughter travels inside the members also?

When I requested her to clarify what exactly she meant by laughter travelling inside, she fumbled a little as it was evident that she had not prepared herself for such a question. But, making some effort she said that what she really meant was that to be Laughter Club members in the true sense, they should develop the spirit of laughter also. I thanked her for the suggestion and assured her that it would be considered seriously. To be honest, I did this first to be polite, but her suggestion did not leave me, because while I had got used to calls imparting critical comments, this was the first time some one had, I felt, made a constructive suggestion. On further reflection, the lady's suggestion struck me as very profound. After all, I asked myself, was it not true that laughter would not add up to anything very much, if a person did not shed at least some of his negativity?

After some serious discussion amongst those involved in the movement, it was decided that the aims of Laughter Clubs be revised from "laugh and be healthy" to "health and happiness through laughter and the spirit of laughter", the spirit of laughter being making not only one's own self happy but also making others happy. Some members interpret this as laughter and the spirit of the laughter becoming a part of the life and living of members.

The above I consider to be an important step along the route of the Laughter Club movement, as it brought about a qualitative extension to the focus of the efforts and the action at Laughter Clubs. We now tried to identify actions as steps which would make not only the members happy but would also motivate and equip them to make others happy.

Looking back, I thought it would be a good idea to do something about those members who come for a daily guffaw and had not changed. I thought this was a wonderful platform where people meet every day and it would be a good idea to adopt some resolutions, to bring about changes in their thinking. The idea was to change negative thinking into positive. We started looking for negative emotions and habits which stop us from laughing.

PAYING COMPLIMENTS

One common bad habit most people have is criticizing others just to kill time or just for the heck of it. During morning walks, the common topics of discussion are politics, the price rise, government corruption, pollution, traffic jams, the bad economy etc., followed by problems relating to youngsters and other family members. I could not stop every one of them. But, I thought of replacing negative thoughts with positive ones. To do away with the habit of criticising others, why not start complimenting

Executives of Volvo Automobiles enjoying a laughter session in Sweden

others and raise their spirits and self esteem? One fine day, I made an announcement after a laughter session was over. "Ladies and gentlemen, today is Monday, and every Monday we are going to resolve that during the week we will pay compliments to others. We will appreciate their good qualities and make more and more friends in our buildings, offices, social circles, etc."

Paying compliments was the first commandment we introduced in our search for identifying various ways and means of sensible living. On Sundays, after the laughter session, we shared our experiences about paying compliments. To whom had club members paid compliments and what were the results? Intially, the response was not very enthusiastic, but some people thought it was a good idea. Many people found it diffi-cult to pay compliments just like that, as it seemed like flattery and syco-phancy. I repeatedly made announcements that one of the objectives of Laughter Clubs is health and happiness through laughter. The happiness aimed at is, not only to make one's own self happy but also to make others happy which further results in one's own happiness. One of the ways to make others happy is by paying genuine and deserved compliments to others.

Some members got very good results and they started appreciating their spouses and children in the house, while others said good words to their servants. In India very few people appreciate their wives with words, they may feel affection in their hearts but they may not verbalise their feelings. For example very few people actually say to their wives, "I love you". One fine day one of the members went home after the laughter session and told his wife "You are looking very beautiful', as she was getting up from bed. She wondered what has happened to her husband, because he had never said this in the last 25 years of their married life. In the first place he had never told his wife before that she was beautiful, but when he said it, the timing was wrong. Had he said these words when she was dressed in her best before going to a party, it would have made more sense.

A social worker from a Laughter Club said thank you to the bus driver while alighing. Everybody was looking at him, as not many people say thank you to bus drivers, taxi drivers or servants in the house. Inspite of initial ridicule and resistance, people have started imbibing the idea because of repeated announcements and reminders. And there is always resistance to any change even if it is for the better.

I was surprised to know that many people find it very difficult to compliment others. The human tendency, by and large, is to see only the wrong and bad in others, ignoring the good and then to criticize and condemn. As a result of this tendency, a lot of negative energy is generated and there is unpleasantness, bitterness, intemperance, tension and bad relations all round. Therefore, the idea of sharing their experiences with compliment-paying was to give members an insight on how to gracefully give compliments. How many things can you compliment and in what ways? The most important thing we tell our members, is to look for good qualities in others and then appreciate them. Giving irrelevant, undeserved, unnecessary compliments might look like a gimmick or pure sycophancy.

Is Paying Compliments Necessary?

People of all ages and backgrounds and at all stages of success and failure need love and recognition in order to live happily. Everyone, if he is to function at his best, needs to be noticed and appreciated. Most of us want to be told how we are doing. If our best efforts are met with silence, we tend to become careless, negligent and hostile.

Each one of us has a mental picture of ourselves, a self image. To find life reasonably satisfying, the self image must be one that we can live with and can like. When we are proud of our self image, we feel confident and free to be ourselves. We function at our best. When we are ashamed of our self image, we attempt to hide rather than express ourselves. In such a situation one becomes hostile and hard to get along with. A sort of miracle happens to the person whose self-esteem has been raised. He suddenly starts liking other people better. He becomes kinder and more co-operative with people around him. Praise is a like a polish that helps to keep one's self image bright and sparkling. By raising someone's spirits and adding to someone's self-esteem you make him want to like you and co-operate with you. To flatter or put into words emotions we don't feel amounts to insincerity which is easily spotted and benefits none.

Withholding a compliment is cheating. It should be passed on as quickly as possible. It might give some unhappy person a moment of joy or help him cope with deep despair. It will help someone defeat the two arch enemies of human happiness - loneliness and insignificance.

Happiness Comes Back

As an artist finds joy in giving beauty to others, so also, anyone who masters the art of praising will find that it blesses the giver as much as the receiver. There is a truth in the saying that "Flowers leave part of their fragrance in the hands that bestow them". If you increase your sense of gratitude and your willingness to express it, you will make the people around happier and you will become a happier person yourself.

How to Pay Compliments

One can pass on compliments in a casual conversation, or in a letter, or a written note. There is yet an other way - that of third party compliments.

When someone says something pleasant to you directly, there is possibility of that being discounted as mere politeness or even flattery. There are many others who find it difficult to pay compliments directly as it may cause some embarrassment. They can take recourse to what may be called 'third party compliments'. This form of appreciation is much easier and could even be more effective. When indirect compliments reach the concerned party they may be better than direct ones, because most people believe that if someone praises you behind your back, he probably means exactly what he says.

WHEN TO PAY COMPLIMENTS

The golden rule of appreciation is - Do it now! Do it while your sense of gratitude is fresh and strong. If you feel a flash of thankfulness, act on it before the impulse goes away.

A FEW EXAMPLES FROM LAUGHTER CLUBS

Though the idea of paying compliments has not taken off fully, it has already made a good beginning. I would like to cite a few stories.

1. There is a cobbler who sits at the corner of the lane where I live in Mumbai. I found him fully involved and happy doing shoe repairing jobs. One fine day I stopped for a while and wanted to express my feelings about him. I said, "My dear sir, you are doing yeoman service to humanity. Do you know that the job you are doing for a few paise, is considered a dirty job by many people?" He smiled and was thrilled to receive such a compliment. After that he smiles at me whenever I pass his shop. I could clearly see his spirits raised by my acknowledging his contribution to society.

2. On Sundays, during our extra meeting to share the secret, one member said, "I didn't pay compliments to anyone but once when I was beginning to criticize someone my inner voice suddenly stopped me saying, Hey! Hey!! What are you doing? You are a Laughter Club member and you are supposed to compliment others!" That was an achievement I believe.

To conclude, what the Laughter Clubs really seeks to achieve is not only laughter outside us but also laughter within us. Paying compliments would result in what we would like to call "Inner laughter", that is "the spirit of laughter''. I often ask Laughter Club members during our monthly meetings, "Why does one go on to make a lot of money, beyond what's needed for one's basic necessities?" It is to get appreciated and noticed. Building a palatial house has no meaning if you don't hold parties and have more and more people appreciate your achievements and taste.

If you spend huge amounts of money only to get appreciation and recognition, there is no need to break your heart in earning that much money. If people spend so much of money in search of compliments, why not give them free and liberally?

On behalf of the Laughter Club International, we are building a network of like-minded people who will share their experiences about complimenting others and we plan to publish a book on ''How to Compliment Others in How Many Ways?'' This would provide a wealth of knowledge from which millions of people would draw inspiration in order to spread happiness. The idea of paying compliments is nothing new. But through the platform of Laughter Clubs it will get manifested rather than remain mere knowledge. By paying compliments, we the members of Laughter Clubs, are developing a conscious habit of praising others and winning hearts. Indirectly, it will help to shun the habit of criticizing others which creates a hostile atmosphere and stops us from laughing.

CHAPTER - 16

Sensible Living:
What has Forgiveness to
do with Laughter Clubs?

L aughter in Laughter Clubs is not meant to be only outer laughter or physical exercise, but also inner laughter, that is, developing the spirit of laughter by being happy and making others happy. It is a joint effort to search for different formulas for stress-free living. To live in peace and hormony, we need to identify and be aware all the time of what stops us from laughing. Going through the various aspects of human behaviour, it was found that there is an entity called the Ego which gets hurt over and again and makes our lives miserable, inspite of our best achievements. Regarding the strange behaviour of human beings, something which has puzzled me though the years is that it takes years to build a relationship and it needs just one stroke to sever age old ties. Friends and relatives become foes and set out to finish each other, the very same people who earlier could not live without each other. What makes all that difference and causes a change of heart? I was told by my learned friends, it is ego.

We all go through life in a world where even well-meaning people hurt one another. A friend insults or betrays, a parent abuses, a lover ditches and so on. That gives rise to a stream of painful memories. If these grudges and grievances are not forgiven, the rancours and resentments keep the old wounds alive. They continue to haunt and harm both parties, physically as well as psychologically. As preached extensively in Jainism, Christianity and many other religions, forgiveness breaks the grip of pain on our minds and opens the doors to the possibility of repairing resentments and grievances, whereas, hate and revenge are totally counterproductive. In the long run, apologising/forgiving is the best alternative for both the forgiver and the forgiven.

But, it is all easier said than done. Still, there is something deep inside us which stops us from asking for forgiveness even if we want to. It feels humiliating for most people to give an apology. And many people find it difficult to forgive others who have caused a grevious hurt. Even if the hurt is well recognised by both parties, then the question arises, who will ask for forgiveness first?

FACTORS WHICH HINDER APOLOGY/FORGIVENESS

There are certain misconceptions, which hinder recourse to the best alternative of apology/forgiveness. Let us review these misconceptions more realistically, as this will help overcome hurdles.

a) The first misconception is that apologising will depict the apologiser as a weak person and may invite humiliation. This is incorrect and contrary to experience. It is the impression of one who has not tried it earlier. The fact is, however, that apologising requires a lot of moral courage and instead of humiliating, it raises the apologiser in the eyes of the other, which prompts the latter to consider forgiving.

b) The apologiser feels doubtful about whether the forgiver will accept his apology. Actually, most people are understanding and when one admits that he is at fault, it touches the generosity instinct which every

Albert Bensimon from Australia with a group of Laughter Club members from Jogger's Park in Bandra, Mumbai.

person has. Even if your apology is rejected once, it may be due to the deep hurt or sensitivity of a person. If persistent efforts are applied, most people will not resist and you will definitely get a chance for peaceful co-existence. If your apology is not accepted, perhaps your expression was not repentant enough to assuage the hurt of the other person.

c) The natural response to deep and unfair hurt is hate, which comes more easily and gives rise to the desire for getting even and hurting back. Therefore, on the face of it, forgiving requires the forgiver to be contrary to his interests and appeals to him to be unnatural and unjust, as his sense of fairness tells him that people must pay for their wrong-doings. For these reasons, the forgiver thinks that forgiving is weakness. These feelings and emotions may be correct on the surface but when examined in depth, it becomes clear that to forgive is to be tough and not weak. It needs a lot of guts to let alone a person who has done harm to you. Though the idea of forgiving may appear to be passive to some, genuine forgiveness is a positive act that requires enormous spiritual strength. Therefore, people who ask for an apology and those who consider forgiveness are not ordinary people. It needs a very stable mind to understand in depth the future implications of hate and revenge. In contrast, if the apology is asked for or forgiveness is considered out of fear that the other person may be stronger, the results may not be fruitful in the long run.

d) Another problem which hinders forgiveness is that one person may keep on hurting the other and ask for forgiveness over and again. If this is happening, the forgiver may choose his stand and communicate it to the apologiser emphatically. But one must not think about this possibility in the very first case.

e) Forgiveness becomes very easy if you analyse the situation and find out if the act of wrongdoing is deliberate or unintended. Calm consideration of the matter will make the hurt person see the truth and then seriously consider the best alternative of forgiveness. Even if the hurt is deliberate, a proper communication of your desire to live in peace will make the other person realise his mistake.

It is very rare the that the wrong-doer is a hundred percent at fault and the person hurt is a hundred per cent innocent. If someone has insulted or hurt you, look deep into yourself to ascertain if your actions, in a small way, were responsible for the act. If you can see your contributions, however small, it becomes much easier to forgive. No person is all good or all bad and everyone has some good and some bad in him. But in practice the application of this truth is one sided. If I am the wrong-doer, to minimise the wrong done by me, I say, "I am not as bad as I am being made out to be. After all there is so much good in me." This is very conveniently forgotten and overlooked when the wrong-doer is someone else. His wrongdoings get exaggerated and good points are ignored. If the forgiver reminds himself that the other person also has something good, it becomes much easier to consider apology or forgiveness.

An Effective Apology

Many times apologies are not considered for forgiveness because they are not projected properly. Naturally, an apology must be sincere and satisfy the forgiver for better results. Otherwise the entire effort may go to waste. For an apology to be effective, the following points should be kept in mind.

a) The apology should be direct and the apologiser should never pretend to be doing something else.

b) The forgiver has to be made to realise that the apology is really meant. Therefore, the apologiser must not be looking at the ground or elsewhere, but into the eyes of the forgiver, though it may be a bit embarrassing for a moment.

c) The apologiser must show readiness to accept responsibility. It should be a total acceptance. One should avoid making excuses because that dilutes the apology. A no excuses apology leaves both the parties feeling better about themselves.

d) Most of the time, it may not be enough to merely say "I am sorry" because the victim wants to see that the apologiser is really feeling bad and looks upset. If the apologiser can put a bit more expression into his apology it is more likely to calm down the recipient.

EFFECTIVE FORGIVENESS

Like an ineffective apology, ineffective forgiveness can also render all efforts fruitless. For forgiveness to be effective:

a) It must be gracious.

b) It must be sincere and show a change of heart on the part of the forgiver.

c) It must not appear as if being done as a favour to the apologiser. It must not be accompanied by warnings or threats. Rather, it should suggest that the apologiser avoids such provocations in future so that both can live in peace and harmony.

d) Acceptance of an apology is very important. Therefore, the forgiver must be seen to be really accepting it. Since most people find it difficult to apologise, the acceptance could be by words like, "I know it must have been hard for you to apologise and I very much appreciate your saying that." It could be by inviting the other party for a cup of tea. Another effective acceptance is by writing a letter with will have better registration. Such symbolic gestures can strengthen the bond of forgiveness. Holding of the hand and a couple of hugs, if appropriate, will add flavour to the future relationship.

NEVER RE-OPEN OLD FILES

The two words 'forgive and forget' generally go together. And rightly so, because if the forgiver is not able to forget, he would not have really forgiven. Forgetting takes some time. That, however, is no cause for worry, because if there is genuine forgiving, the wounds will heal and forgetting will eventually come. Forgetting, however, does not mean obliterating the whole event from memory. What has to be forgotten is the hurt, resentment and bitterness. Details of the happenings, which remain in the memory, without bitterness and hurt, could serve the useful purpose of enabling others to learn from the experience. All the best efforts will be nullified if one tries to open old files at the slightest provocation. I have seen people making each other's lives miserable for years together, referring to an event which had happened twenty years before.

To illustrate this point we narrate and enact a story as to how hunters catch monkeys. They fix a box with iron bars placed at such a distance that a monkey can put in his empty hand to take the bananas kept inside. Once the monkey holds a banana, it becomes difficult for him to pull his hand out of the box. If it has the wisdom of leaving the banana it could go free. By holding on to the banana, he gets caught. In our workshops we actually tell one of the participants to hold a banana and try to take his hand out, which does not happen. Taking a cue from the story, we remind our members: Whenever you make the mistake of opening old grievances, remember that you are acting like a monkey holding on to his banana.

ADVANTAGES OF APOLOGY/FORGIVENESS

Experts have come to realise that forgiving and forgetting is one of the first means of defence. These are untapped and least understood sources of healing power.

a) If a person realises his mistake, but does not pick up the courage to apologise, that does not benefit him any way. Rather, he is perpetuating endless self-punishment. Seeking forgiveness can free him of that punishment.

b) In a strained relationship both the parties live under stress. An apology and forgiveness can result in new happiness for both.

c) It breaks pain's grip on our minds and opens the doors for new possibilities. A new beginning could arise from past pain.

d) Forgiveness transforms hostility into helpfulness and lifts the spirits of both the forgiver and the forgiven.

e) It is said that the most important ingredient in forgiveness is love, and at its best, forgiveness is done for those persons who are our loved ones and have hurt us. Forgiveness, in such cases, is at its most powerful, renewing friendships, marriages and careers.

f) Hate and revenge disturb the harmony of the entire family. Hate, whether passive or active, is a malignancy that grows, eats you from within and keeps on releasing harmful chemicals that give rise to a battery of illnesses. And vegeance never evens the score. It leads to an endless spate of retaliation. History is full of such examples, where a little act of revenge has wiped out entire families and has led to war between nations. Mahatma Gandhi once said that if we all live by an "eye for an eye" kind of justice, the whole of mankind would be blind.

DOUBLE BENEFIT

There are many situations in life where one is provoked into a state of anger. If you get angry with someone who is bothering you and fight with him unavoidably, there is a lot to be achieved by saying 'sorry' after sometime when your temple has cooled down. You may fire your child, your family member, an employee or a neighbour. They will have hurt feelings even if they are not able to express then. But if you pick up the courage to go up to the person with whom you fought a short while earlier and say, "Sorry. I got angry with you, but I got upset because I didn't like the way you behaved with me." Here, by saying sorry you are

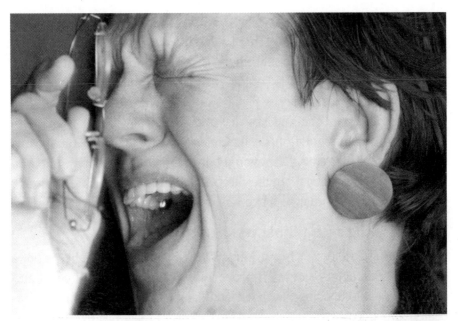

Laughter during laughter meditation becomes very intense and deep, the kind of laughter we rarely experience in daily life.

neutralising the hurt feeling inflicted by your outburst and you can take this opportunity to remind the person once again, about the reason why you got angry.

FRIDAY FOR FORGIVENESS

In the Jain religion there is a festival once a year called *"Michhami Dukkadam"* meaning asking for forgiveness. On one particular day, after prayers in the temple, people ask for forgiveness from each other. Also there are forgiveness cards like new year greeting cards, which are sent out to relatives, friends and business colleagues asking for forgiveness, if they have been hurt directly or indirectly. Since ancient days, it has been a good platform for those who feel inhibited to verbalise their apologies directly to the people concerned.

I attended one such function and was highly impressed with the idea, and thought it worthwhile to implement forgiveness through Laughter Clubs. Somewhere in March 1997, I explained this idea to the members and most of them liked it. Doing this once a year might not help to register this idea, and it may take too long to experiment with various practical aspects of it. Therefore, I thought, why not remind the members every Friday, even though there is no relation of a particular day with forgiveness? Every Friday the anchor person makes an announcement, "Dear Friends, today is Friday, our forgiveness day. If you think you have hurt someone and you have not been on talking terms with somebody for a long time, this is the time to muster up some courage and offer an apology, saying, "Knowingly or unknowingly if I have hurt you in any way, I am sorry." Invite the person for a cup of tea or to come over for dinner, in order to make a new beginning.

LAUGHTER CLUBS AND FORGIVENESS

Designating Friday as "Forgiveness Day" by Laughter Clubs, is not a gimmick or an empty slogan. If properly implemented, it will be a valuable means of enhancing the inner laughter of members. By making repeated announcements and doing a sort of dress rehearsal every Friday, the chances of getting this idea registered are much higher. The trouble with most people is that even if they want to say sorry, it is difficult to verbalise these feelings. By doing it over and again we are making it a conscious habit so that apologies come out easily when required. I myself have been benefited immensely from this idea. I must have renewed over dozen relationships by giving an apology. As a matter of fact, many bonds have become much stronger than before.

WHAT DOES NOT CONSTITUTE FORGIVENESS?

Forgiveness is the ability to control anger by understanding the situation in depth and then choosing the right kind of response instead of a prompt reaction. It prevents generation of anger and enables one to control the emotion of revenge. Forgiveness is kindness, tenderness, affinity and love expressed after careful thought.

Hypocrisy is to forgive outwardly and cultivate revenge, enmity and a desire to punish inwardly. It is not forgiveness. If one forgives under the threat that "My enemy or opponent may harass me if I don't forgive," it is not real forgiveness. If greed and temptation are motives behind forgiving: "If I don't forgive my motive will not be served", then it is not real forgiveness. If your ego is dictating forgiveness. "I am powerful, I am the master and only I can forgive him and save him and in return can get things done to my convenience", it is not forgiveness. In short, forgiveness originating from ego, fear, hypocrisy, greed, lust etc. is not real forgiveness. Selfless, motiveless, unperverted manifestations of love, kindness and affection constitute forgiveness.

Laugh Like
a Genie

Laugh Like a Red Indian

CHAPTER - 17

Laughter Clubs:
Now Developing into
Close-knit Communities

Ongoing research shows that people suffering from depression are more prone to many illnesses like high blood pressure, heart attacks and cancer. Depression also affects the immune system adversely. Common causes of depression are social isolation and a diminishing family value system. These are more frequent in western countries but are now slowly affecting the east also. Laughter Clubs have helped many people to get rid of their antidepressant pills in a short period of time. The magic which has worked wonders is the friendship and brotherhood gained from Laughter Clubs. Laughter Clubs are fast developing into close-knit communities.

Laughter is an important tool in our social interaction. It is not only a biological release or a cognitive process, but more importantly it is a social psychological phenomenon, which initiates and facilitates communication. With the spread of Laughter Clubs in every locality, each club has taken the shape of a small community, wherein its members experience a sense of affiliation and belonging to the group. Clubs are turning into large "Laughing Families"

SOCIAL GLUE

The affiliation, in more than one way, has been positive for most members. These clubs are now not only responsible for enhancement of physical health, but also for safeguarding emotional health and, more importantly, communicating harmoniously. Laughter is a common language. It knows no religion and has no gender bias. There is no discrimination according to caste, creed or colour. Laughter is a powerful emotion and a social glue. When Steve Wilson, a psychologist and joyologist from the United States visited some Laughter Clubs in Mumbai, he had the unique experience of participating in a laughter session at Juhu Beach.

In a matter of the few minutes that he spent laughing with so-called strangers, it appeared at the end of the session, as if he knew everyone in that group. There was a strange feeling of closeness with them. Many of our visitors from all over the world share similar views. Thinkers, whether they are sociologists, psychologists, behaviourists or historians for that matter, have always believed that 'Man is a social animal'. We are very well aware of the fact that our behaviour is the result of social values and norms and we all survive on the basis of our social interactions. And there is no doubt that sociability of any kind is considered definitely worth cultivating.

Research conducted in various fields has provided mounting evidence to support the fact that people who belong to a network of community, friends and relatives are happier and healthier, better able to cope with stress and remarkably resistant to emotional and physical ills. Each Laughter Club, with no monetary inclination, has become a close-knit community where people enjoy the caring and warmth of its members. More important, people form close ties with others, irrespective of the economic stratum they belong to.

Prof. Dennis T. Jaffe, Ph. D., a Professor of Psychology at Saybook Institute in San Francisco, has found that, "A close-knit community can

152

The members of the Laughter Clubs are like a extended family.

act as a protective envelope against stresses of environment." Belonging to the Indian subcontinent we are very fortunate, since our culture supports the family value system. But now a growing western influence has slowly started taking its toll. Today, due to materialization, people have become more self-centered and socially isolated with a rapidly changing social system. Even the way in which we view our elders has changed. A feeling of being worthy and of importance to others is essential, not only for a person's self esteem but also for emotional health. When an individual is younger this is a natural experience, because a family is dependent on one another irrespective of whether one is a man or a woman.

Being a man one is more often looked upon for economic security and being a woman, for ensuring a happy, well settled home. Though this pattern is not a given rule, it is not uncommon either. But when there is a transition from youth to old age, this is when perception changes. Evidence from research suggests that in communities where elders are considered a source of wisdom, they are not abandoned, as is the case in other societies. The mortality rates are much lower when compared to other societies. In Laughter Clubs, a majority of members are from an older group, but nowadays many youngsters have also started coming in because of the value addition and health benefits.

ISOLATION IS SICKNESS

In a recent study, participants said they had experienced ties within a Laughter Club such as those in every close-knit family, wherein not only an individual's happiness but also one's sorrows are shared. And hence, it is this sense of social worth that is reinforced by belonging to an accepting and caring community. We ask ourselves the question: What acts as a buffer to stress? The answer is: Our spouses, our friends, our siblings, in other words, our social network.

In modern society, where social isolation is becoming a sickness, Laughter Clubs are a welcome introduction to bring back the social value system. I am proud to say that the friendship and brotherhood in Laughter Clubs have made people much more secure than their non-member relatives and friends. I would like to quote an example of a senior member from the Johnson Garden Laughter Club, who fell sick and was admitted to hospital. He burst into tears of joy when he found his room flooded with flowers from visitors from the Laughter Club, when none of his family members and relatives turned up.

A TOUCHING INCIDENT

Another incident which I will never forget is when I visited the Laughter Club of Bandra Reclamation in Mumbai, where members laugh everyday in the compound of a temple. At the end of one particular laughter session, the birthday celebrations of a 78-year-old lady were held. This club has a unique way of celebrating birthdays. All the members surrounded the "birthday baby" and sang a happy birthday song for her and danced around her in a circle. Later, she was taken to the temple a few yards away where she was made to sit on a chair in front of the Ganpati idol. She was offered a coconut, flowers and sweets by the priest and then many Laughter Club members touched her feet (a sign of respect in India). Throughout the celebrations, tears were rolling down her cheeks. They were nothing but tears of joy. I had read in books about these tears and was now fortunate enough to see them in reality. This is the Laughter Club we are talking about. This is the Laughing Family the whole world is awaiting. A Laughter Club, in many ways, provides a protective shell that safeguards our emotional well-being. And it is because of this emotional well-being that we can have a physiologically sound system that would determine our resistance to disease. Laughter Clubs have brought a lot of people together, the consequence being an awareness that one is not alone with one's problems.

How Laughter Club Members Socialise

The process of socializing starts from the beginning, the day the member joins the Laughter Club. Most laughter sessions are held at public parks, beaches and open grounds where people go for their morning walks. In our initial survey we found that the same people who were laughing together used to come for a morning walk for years and never knew each other. They came closer when they started laughing together. Laughter is a powerful positive emotion and it changes the electromagnetic fields around your body and builds a positive aura. Due to laughter in a group, inhibitions are broken down and a person becomes more receptive. And it is a very happy socialising that keeps growing as one laughs more and more. It brings about nearness, companionship and camaraderie, flowering into a kind of social support.

Celebrations

Laughter groups have started celebrating different festivals belonging to all communities in their own styles. This has helped to bring about communal harmony amongst members. Like this, throughout the year club members meet at least once in two months. They sing, they dance and they eat together, without any discrimination between rich and poor.

Fun Games

With more than 25,000 members in less than four years, Laughter Clubs are being recognised as a public movement. Though there is no membership fee, we organise seminars, health workshops, yoga and meditation camps from time to time. Many companies come forward to sponsor these events to gain public milage. Fun games are regularly organised where members have fun-filled healthy competition with each other, let themselves go and enjoy the warmth of each other's company.

OUTINGS AND PICNICS

Outings and picnics in a big group have their own fun, especially if participants are all Laughter Club members. Most clubs organise outings, picnics and excursions and feel happy together. They sing, dance and play fun games and have some new idea or another because there is no dearth of new ideas in such a big group. People have admitted that group picnics are much more enjoyable than family picnics. Another added advantage is gaining massive group discounts. They can have much more for the same amount of money.

All tourist places offer heavy discounts to Laughter Club members, sensing the big potential of regular business from them. The extent of socialising through Laughter Clubs can be gauged by the frequency and extent of participation in the outings. Many groups organise trips for 3-4 days, several times a year.

In between there are one-day picnics, at least once in two months. Now the frequency is on the rise as members are exploring new destinations all over the country. The formats of picnics are being shared by different club members to make them more interesting and enjoyable. Through our central body, the Laughter Club International, we are sharing all the good things in life to keep motivation levels high.

HOLIDAY-CUM-LEARNING

In our new model outings, we are trying to make our holidays more value-based by adding health-building activities like learning yoga, meditation, acupressure and different non-drug, alternative healing systems. It is 75% fun and 25% learning. With our ever expanding network we are introducing new projects to add more colour to Laughter Clubs.

CELEBRATING BIRTHDAYS

Many members are senior citizens and they had long abandoned the idea of celebrating their birthdays. Now they have suddenly come alive.

A group of ladies laughing their stress away.

There are many members who have celebrated their birthdays for the first time in their lives. Why not be proud of our existence? In Laughter Clubs, birthdays are celebrated in a very simple and affectionate manner. Some do it with the usual song sung in chorus and by presenting flowers, others give out special greeting cards made on a computer. In some cases, talented members compose a special poem for the occasion. There is yet another way: to make the member wear a funny cap and give him a whistle to blow. This is just a beginning, wait and watch for more ideas. You will be surprised at how creative Laughter Club members can become.

PROJECT "*CHALO CINEMA*" (GO FOR MOVIES)

On April 1, 1999, we celebrated All Fools Day - the idea was to make fun of yourself and try to laugh at yourself. It was a hilarious function, the details of which are given in another chapter. On that day we launched yet another social project "Chalo Cinema". The theme of this project is to go out for a movie in a group. With the advent of television and cable networks, people have forgotten to visit theatres which used to provide much needed outings for many. People have become too lazy to go for a movie alone, or with the family, as different members have their own engagements.

INTER CLUB EXCHANGE PROGRAMMES

Socialisation is not restricted among the members of a particular Laughter Club but goes beyond that. While celebrating anniversaries, invitations are extended to other clubs in town. Representatives of different groups are called and honoured during the function. Not only that, some groups even go for picnics together. This is further strengthening the relationship between the members of various clubs.

Extending this idea further, we have started inter-club exchange programmes under which a group of Laughter Club members (generally 10-20) would visit other cities and the host club would arrange to provide them with a home-stay on a voluntary basis. The visiting team would have to pay for their travel arrangements. The boarding, lodging and sight-seeing would be looked after by the host club. This will provide Laughter Club members from all over the country with the opportunity to visit different places and while staying with families, they would understand different cultures. This arrangement is entirely on a mutual basis. The visiting members who enjoy a family stay must reciprocate by hosting people from other cities.

Slowly, when we set up Laughter Clubs all over the world, it will provide an opportunity for the world community to come together and visit different countries in a most economical and interesting way. This project is still in its experimental stages. Some groups have already visited each other with encouraging results. In India I see very bright prospects as Indians are very hospitable people. I am sure we will be successful on an international platform too.

CHAPTER - 18

Laughter Therapy in the Workplace

The growing popularity of Laughter Clubs all over India, and the interest shown by many who have visited these clubs from all over the world have made one point very clear - these clubs are no laughing matter. While tens of thousands are taking to this unique therapy, there are many who wished to join a Laughter Club, but could not do so because of time constraints. Most clubs start quite early, between 6.30 a.m. and 7 a.m. and they are held at public parks where people go for a morning walk. This is the time many office goers cannot come, because they have to leave early for office. Quite a few women cannot participate because they have to send their children to school and their husbands to office.

I was inspired by the idea from some companies in Japan where it is a regular practice to do some physical exercises in the office premises in

A laughter session at Glaxo Pharmaceuticals' Thane factory, near Mumbai.

the morning, before employees start their work. All the members of the company, from Managing Director to peons, participate. We believe that introducing Laughter Therapy in corporate houses is a very significant and worthwhile idea. It can help to improve inter-personal relationships at all levels in an organization, replacing mutual lack of trust and confidence with a more positive outlook and a co-operative attitude towards one's colleagues and subordinates. This should, in turn, definitely help to improve the prevalent work environment and overall performance of an organization.

FEAR OF INDISCIPLINE

Initially, many people showed interest, but such proposals did not materialise because of some hesitation about anything new being started and that too a funny concept. Maybe they feared that this might be ridiculed, or it may cause indiscipline. I wrote to many companies, corporate houses, medium and small sized factories. Many bosses thought the workers might not understand the concept well. Many of them, and rightly so, were waiting for its bonafides to be proved. I went on to give seminars and demonstrations in many offices and factories. I found some resistance from the management, who were not very keen on mixing with their workers, because they feared that the workers might not respect them or might disobey them if they laughed together. Usually, they would send their managers to attend the sessions and they themselves refused to come out of their cabins. Fortunately, this fear was proved wrong when we successfully implemented this programme in many factories and offices in Mumbai. Our laughter leaders in many countries are making presentations on laughter yoga in companies, organisations and corporations.

PRODUCTIVITY THROUGH LAUGHTER

Today business houses and industries all over the world are facing the worst ever recession. Profits are declining and workers are hard pressed to match their incomes with rising prices. Executives are hard pressed to step up sales in the face of fierce competition. Members of the business community (Managers, Sales and Marketing Personnel, Executives, Administrators) are living very stressful lives. It is important to realise that most of our time is spent at the workplace and the maximum amount of stress is also at the workplace. Most diseases like high blood pressure, heart disease, peptic ulcers, insomnia, depression, allergies and even cancer have some relation to stress. This contributes to absenteeism, poor performance and addictions.

ADVANTAGES OF LAUGHTER THERAPY IN CORPORATE HOUSES

❖ Laughter Therapy increases oxygen levels in the body and releases endorphins (feel-good hormones) from the brain cells. Daily laughter exercise will promote a sense of well-being and feeling of freshness throughout the day. Participants learn to wear smiles on their faces.

❖ It will help reduce inhibitions, increase self-confidence and develop leadership qualities among participants. Starting the day on a positive note will improve interpersonal relationships and hence performance. Bosses and subordinates will work with a better frame of mind, rather than fearing each other.

- Deep breathing and neck and shoulder stretching exercises will help remove stiffness and pain resulting from stress and a sedentary life-style.

- Laughter Therapy increases body resistance by stimulating the immune system of the body. Regular laughing sessions will significantly reduce the frequency of coughs, colds and throat and chest infections.

- It will help to control many diseases like high blood pressure, heart disease, irritability, insomnia, anxiety, depression, allergic disorders, asthma, bronchitis, tension and migraine headaches, as well as aches and pains due to arthritis, cervical spondylitis and backache.

- Laughter Therapy is one of the easiest types of meditation and promotes instant relaxation. It disconnects your mind from the physical world. While laughing you cannot think of anything else. In other types of meditation you need to concentrate a lot to take your mind away from unwanted thoughts, which is easier said than done.

- As a group effort, all the Laughter Club members try to identify and remove negative factors like guilt, anger, fear, jealousy and ego, which stop us from laughing. They cultivate the spirit of laughter by following ways and means of sensible living, like paying compliments, the art of forgiveness and understanding human relationships.

- By holding periodic seminars we impart practical training to help members to discover their own sense of humour and celebrate life, in spite of its tough challenges.

- Through the practice of Yogic Laughter we want to make people understand that happiness and laughter are states of mind and should be unconditional, irrespective of the ups and downs of life. If you are in a happy and positive frame of mind you can solve your problems in a much better way. We want to make people believe in the philosophy that motion creates emotion. If you act like a happy man first thing in the morning your chemistry will become real.

- To make people aware of the power of group effort. Anything practiced in a group becomes easier, as compared to trying to do the same thing alone. Not only do we laugh and do stretching exercises together, we are also learning to understand the ways and means of sensible living all together.

❖ Every human being has infinite potential to perform and achieve anything he desires, but most of his power lies dormant and untapped. Through Laughter Therapy and meditation, one can release one's infinite potential and achieve greater heights in life.

DREAM OF A "LAUGHING ROOM" IN COMPANIES

While I was conducting a seminar in Copenhagen, Denmark, for Hewlett Packard I saw a room called the Smoking Room and suddenly the idea flashed into my mind that if there can be a smoking room in companies, why not a "Laughing Room" where the employees can go and laugh together for 10-15 minutes and feel relaxed.

This is a dream I am carrying in my mind and one day it is going to to be realized. Laughter in the workplace is the only way we can have laughter therapy sessions everyday, or at least five days in a week. Social laughter clubs in western countries laugh once in a week which is good but not enough. To reap concrete effects of laughter therapy quickly one needs to laugh everyday. The advantage of having a laughing room in the workplace is that one they doesn't have to specially invite people for a laughter session. People are already there in the workplace and it becomes much easier to get the required number of participants for a group laughter session.

CHAPTER - 19

Laughter Sessions Among School Children

O ne thing which always embarrassed me was people asking me, "What age group of people come for laughing sessions? The answer was those who are 40 plus, senior citizens and retired people. Does that give the impression that Laughter Clubs are only meant for elderly people who have nothing else to do? Why didn't youngsters come for laughter sessions?

Though school children used to enjoy laughter sessions during their vacations, they were not able to come regularly because most laughter sessions start quite early between 6.30 - 7a.m. This is the time children have to hurry to catch their buses. College classes too start quite early and most youngsters are not aware of the benefits of laughter therapy. They think it is more for those who are suffering from some kind of ailment. Moreover they are interested in heavy workouts like jogging, swimming, gymnastics, cycling and aerobics. Nowadays many middle-

aged women have started coming as they have found laughter to be very beneficial. Among the participants in many clubs there were school teachers and they kept experimenting with small groups of children in their schools, but nobody came up with a solid proposal. The apprehension about implementing laughter exercise could be the fear of the nuisance children might create during their classes. But if it is projected as a authentic yogic exercise and done in a properly structured manner and executed by popular teachers, it will definitely bring good results.

THE FIRST PROPOSAL

One fine day I received a telegram from Mr. Madhukar Parashar, Principal of Progressive English High School, Aurangabad, in Maharashtra State, inviting me to start yogic laughter for school children. "I want to see my children smiling when they enter their classes," said Mr. Parashar. He had read about the Laughter Clubs of Mumbai in several newspapers. The principal was so keen about laughter that he introduced a few jokes in the morning after prayers, to make his pupils laugh. He kept on calling me over the telephone and sent me a couple of telegrams requesting me to visit his school at the earliest. I distinctly remember the date. It was 21st October 1996, the day I was waiting to start my first session with 300 boys and girls between the ages of 4 and 15, along with about 50 parents and 25 school teachers. Everybody was waiting in suspense to see what was going to happen in the next hour. I have always loved making children laugh, because it is easy to make them giggle and chuckle. During the demonstration they were bursting with laughter and sometimes it was very difficult to stop them. I wanted them to be quiet before we could demonstrate the next type of laughter. I requested the principal and senior teachers to keep them quiet. In my four years of experience, I have observed that when I am with adults, I tell them, "Come on, Laugh! Laugh!" and they find it difficult to laugh. But whenever I went to any school for a laughter session, I found it difficult to stop the children laughing. They would laugh at any silly thing.

One very striking feature was that younger children, below the age of six, were less inhibited and were laughing more vibrantly than their senior schoolmates. Teachers were also enjoying the session but they too were a bit inhibited. The head teacher and P.T. teacher took the intiative of learning the various techniques so as to continue laughter sessions everyday for 5 to 10 minutes after the school prayers in the morning. The children were overjoyed and showed their willingness to laugh everyday.

The very next day we left Aurangabad and we were kept updated with encouraging reports of laughter sessions in the school. Many children wrote me letters requesting me to come again. This was the only school which practiced laughter everyday. But my joy didn't last long enough. After one year when I visited Aurangabad for a stress management workshop in an industrial house, I discovered that the Principal Mr. Parashar had had a heart attack a few months previously and due to his demise the laughter sessions had stopped. After that, the caretaker of the school didn't take any intiative to start such sessions again.

Following that I must have given demonstrations in more than 25 schools in various cities. The concept was appreciated but so far none has imple-

A laughter session with disabled children in a school at Perth, Australia.

mented it. Maybe they are waiting for its bonafides to be proved. Maybe they are afraid of the nuisance the children might create. Meanwhile, many teachers are trying out laughter sessions in the classes in a small way and finding it very useful in creating a positive mood.

WHY CHILDREN OF TODAY NEED TO LAUGH MORE

a) While children are said to be the ideal models of mirth, too much stress of modern studies has taken a toll of their laughter, it seems. They are loaded with too much information. The subjects which we were taught in the 10th standard, poor kids are now forced to study in the 5th standard. Competition is very tough these days, and to stay in the race they have to cut down on their play time and attend extra tutions. Thus, their stress levels are mounting. More and more children are committing suicide because they can't stand the fierce competition. Laughter sessions everyday will help to reduce these stress levels.

b) Today's children abandon the spirit of fun, play and laughter at an early age. This was very obvious when we had combined sessions with children from the 1st to 10th standards. While children below the 3rd and 4th standards were having a great time, the seniors were a bit more reserved. Daily laughter will help them retain their spirit of laughter and playfulness.

c) Children of today will have to face tough challenges to survive in this competitive world. If they can be taught to handle their emotions effectively and learn the ways and means of sensible living through laughter therapy, they can live much happier lives.

BENEFITS OF LAUGHTER THERAPY TO CHILDREN

1. Regular laughter sessions will increase oxygen supply to improve their mental functions and academic performance.

2. It will reduce stress during examination time. Before entering the exam hall, they should be made to laugh for 10 minutes to reduce anxiety.

3. Laughter Therapy will increase stamina and breathing capacity to help them excel in sports activities. It will be very relaxing before competitive sports events.

4. It will increase the level of relaxation and reduce nervousness and stage fright. It will also help children to be more extrovert and develop self-confidence.

5. They will suffer fewer attacks of coughs, colds, throat and chest infections, as laughter helps to build good immunity against common infections.

6. If yogic deep breathing is practised in between two types of laughter, it will help them develop mental stability. If cheerfulness becomes a way of life, they will have a positive attitude even during hard times. Laughter will also help them enhance their creative abilities.

CHAPTER - 20

Laughing Session with the Blind: a Wonderful Experience

T here was a time in the initial two years when every week some news or the other about Laughter Clubs used to appear in various newspapers and magazines. For media people the idea of Laughter Clubs was fascinating. In October 1997, I remember receiving a phone call from Mr. Dinesh Saryia, requesting me to come to an institute for the blind in Dadar, Mumbai, and demonstrate the laughter techniques for 60-80 young girls, most of whom were below 12 years. Mr. Saryia told me, "We have heard a lot about your Laughter Clubs, why not make blind people laugh?"

Dinesh must have been around 25 and his vision was diminishing due to retinitis pigmentosa, a disease which gradually leads to blindness. He expressed his desire to meet me in my office and work out the details. I said yes a bit hesitantly, because I was wondering how I would make blind people laugh.

Normally, we laugh in a group and stimulate each other by looking into each other's eyes. This is how we are able to convert forced laughter into genuine chuckles. After two days young Dinesh came to my office with a colleague who was blind too. They spent nearly half-an-hour with me and one thing which was very peculiar was that while talking they were smiling all the time, which is very rare in normal individuals. Suddenly I recalled my visits to blind homes during my college days when I observed that most blind people have inbuilt smiles on their faces when they talk, for what reason I don't know. I was also aware of the fact the blind people become extraordinarily talented in music, weaving skills and other arts. Both the youngsters were very happy and enthusiastic about our visit to the blind home. I went along with four Laughologists by local train and it took us half-an-hour to find the institute in that congested locality.

We were given a warm welcome at the Institute's Annual Readers Day function, where we found many normal young volunteers who were committed to helping the blind students. Throughout the year whenever they got spare time they came and read to blind students. After the initial ceremony, we asked a group of 30-40 blind girls to come out in the open and experience the joy of laughing exercise. Initially the little girls were hesitant and giggling among themselves, saying, "How can we laugh like that?" At the same time they were amused with the idea of laughing in a group for no reason. After ten minutes of persuasion they joined the group of adults outside in the compound. I was still not sure, whether I would be able to make them laugh.

THE SOUND OF LAUGHTER IS ALSO CONTAGIOUS

One needs to look at other people to intiate laughter. Eye contact is an important factor in eliciting genuine giggles. But I was proved wrong when I experimented with that particular laughter session.

For the first time I realised that the sound of laughter is also infectious. As the session progressed the quality of laughter improved. The small little girls were laughing non-stop and it was indeed difficult to stop them. They were laughing heartily as if they were starved of this natural gift. So much so, two girls had tears rolling down their cheeks. To my surprise, hesitant looking youngsters were laughing more vibrantly than adults who also joined the session. At the end, quiet looking girls suddenly became talkative and asked me, "Uncle, when will you come again to make us laugh?" I did say I would come back soon, but there was no further response from the organisers. I requested the principal and authorities of the blind institute to carry on laughter sessions every day. I was willing to send a few senior members of Laughter Clubs to train the anchors. But it was not to be. I never got any call from there. To me it seems, those little girls are still waiting for me and one day I will go there, even if uninvited.

This was a unique experience to remember and I would like to bring smiles and laughter to the faces of millions of blind people all over the world. It may bring a fresh ray of hope to their sight-deprived lives. I am determined to form a task force of senior people from Laughter Clubs who want to do some social work and who have plenty of time. I need some funds to implement this scheme. I call upon social workers and philanthropists to join hands with me in this mission.

Laugh Like an Arab

CHAPTER - 21

"Woman Power" in Laughter Clubs

I have always held women in high esteem as far as health is concerned. Man is supposed to be stronger then woman in many ways, but when it comes to health and stress management, women are far ahead of their counterparts. Women have always been more concerned about the health of their families and they are always in the forefront whenever any health-building activity is being considered. One of the unique features of Laughter Clubs is the enthusiastic participation from the fairer sex. In a conservative country like India, it requires a lot of courage for a woman to come out in a public place and laugh aloud for no reason.

In the beginning when we started the first Laughter Club in Mumbai, we had only two women, as others were not sure of what exactly would happen and how useful these funny proceedings would be. Initially, many

Argument laughter is very popular among women all over the world!

women used to watch from a distance and get amused, but they didn't have the courage to join the group as they were waiting for more women to join. Slowly, over a period of time, when we learnt to laugh without jokes and the word started spreading about the breathing and stretching exercises based on yoga, more and more women started participating. Most participants are aged 40-50 plus, as younger women have to send their children to school and their husbands to office. But during vacations they used to come along with their children and enjoyed the fun. Many regretted their non-availability in the mornings.

After working hard in their kitchens and at the chores of running a household, our Laughter Clubs provided a new platform for them to give vent to their bottled-up emotions. I must admit that the presence of more and more women provided authenticity to our movement. People in India believe that if there are women in Laughter Clubs there must be something good about them, otherwise they would not endorse them so enthusiastically.

MORE DEVOTED

In my experience, when it comes to laughing with no reason, it was much easier to make women laugh than men. The absurdity and stupidity factor works better with women. Even the infectiousness of laughter is much better in them. I do not understand the reason for this. Maybe they are less logic-oriented than men. They operate more out of devotion. That is the reason why more women are to be found at spiritual discourses and religious activities.

MORE FUN - LOVING

It may be due to their long association with children while bringing them up, that women are more fun-loving. All the fun activities during various functions conducted by Laughter Clubs are efficiently executed by women. While playing fun games they are more absorbed and they don't look as if they are doing them just to kill time. Recently we launched a new project 'Chalo cinema' (Go for movies), because going to a theatre in a group has its own charm. We advised all club members to go for a movie, drama or to the circus at least once in two months. The project took off very well and again the women were more enthusiastic.

ONLY WOMEN CLUB

There were 30-40 per cent of women in all the Laughter Clubs for a year or so. After that there were some drop-outs among men because of their other commitments, but the attendance of women started growing. In many clubs, women outnumber men. They seem more committed and their drop-out rate is much lower. At many places there are 100% women only clubs!

My joy knew no bounds when I was informed that there was a 'women only club' going very strong in one of the suburbs in Mumbai, where they laugh at 6 p.m. every evening for half-an-hour. Surprisingly, there were 60-70 women gathered in the compound of a building and laughing out loud. Normally, we don't suggest that people start a Laughter Club in a building compound because even if one person complains about noise pollution, the club will land up with problems.

I was told by the confident group leader that there is no chance of any complaint, because members from each and every house come down to participate in the laughter sessions. Seeing is believing. I went there and found amazing enthusiasm. A majority of members were working women. They come back home at 5.30 p.m. and start their guffaws at 6 p.m. I never expected this to happen but I was truly happy to see this development.

LAUGHTER KITTY

Many women who could not join Laughter Clubs in the morning because of their household commitments requested me to start an evening Laughter Club and on 18th July we started with the new concept of a Laughter Kitty. It was very successful because in addition to laughter yoga exercises we could do laughter meditation, followed by fun games and dancing. The most important aspect about the Laughter Kitty is that the members are discussing and sharing their experiences of life. All these things were not possible in public park Laughter Clubs. In Mumbai, the Laughter Kitty concept is becoming very popular and we are getting many request to open such evening Laughter Clubs.

Laughter in the workplace : 35 factory workers start the day with laughter.

Members of an IT company (Lanbit Computers) laughing their way to success in Mumbai.

Women power in Laughter Clubs : More than 70% members are women.
God only knows why!

A laughing Competition in progress in Copenhagen, Denmark.
Jan Thygesen Poulsen and Dr. Kataria look on

Laugh your cancer away : Laughter helps to fight cancer by strengthening the immune system and putting a person in a positive mental state.

A laughter workshop at Hamburg, Germany

Laughter Happy-demic : World Laughter Day 1999 celebrations in Mumbai, India.

World Laughter Day 2001 celebrations in Copenhagen, Denmark. More than 6000 people gathered together, and had a laughter session and prayed for World Peace

A laughter Club in action at Zurich, Switzerland.

Laughter session in progress at Bressels in Belgium

London Laughter Club, UK.

Dr. Kataria with Tony Buzan at the Singapore Learning Festival.

Dr. Kataria conducts a laughter session in Singapore.

A laughter session in progress at the Humour Conference in Stuttgart, Germany.

Corinne Cosseron (South France) along with Marc De Wilde leading
a laughter session in Frontignan

A group of certified laughter leaders in Copenhagen, Denmark.

Celebration time : A happy group of laughter members at the first
All India Laughter Convention LAFF-98 in Goa, India.

Age no bar : Anybody from womb to tomb can join the Laughter Club.

The Laughter Club of Kaula Lampur, Malaysia.

A laughter session with a Japanese delegation.

A laughter seminar in Kalmar, Sweden.

Laughter meditation in progress at Wiesbaden, Germany.

Corinne Cosseron leading a laughter meditation session at
the beach in Frontignan, South France

Daniel Kiefer leading laughter session in oldage home in Soultz, France

It's ALL FOOLS DAY! On 1st April 1999, over 100 anchor persons from various Laughter Clubs of Mumbai, celebrated an event at which everything was funny!

A fun game called "Hammering the husband" made everybody laugh uproariously during Fool's Day celebrations.

Free Laughter meditation session lead by Michel M. Abitbol at
Québec Laughter Club, Montreal, Canada

Essi Tolonen from Finland and Linda from Sweden participating in a rally during All India
Laughter Convention LAFF-2003 in Udaipur, India

Members of the Laughter Club of Brisbane, Australia

Susan Welch, Laughter Club of Qld Director, second from left,
Laughing with some teachers from the department of education in Queensland

CHAPTER - 22

Role of the Anchor Person in a Laughter Club

One of the absolute requirements of running a successful Laughter Club is having an anchor person or a ring leader. There can be more than one anchor person in a group. His job is not to crack jokes and make people laugh, nor is he supposed to do any mimicry or funny actions. His main purpose is to initiate the different stages of laughter, breathing exercises and stretching exercises. He is like a trigger, who laughs more easily and infectiously than others. His job is to motivate others to drop their inhibitions and be more playful, so that stimulated laughter can be converted into genuine peals of hilarity. A humble nature, good self-confidence, proper eye contact and a vibrant voice to give commands to initiate laughter are some of basic qualities he or she must have.

PROPER TRAINING

- Even with all the inbuilt qualities of a good leader, the anchor person needs proper training to conduct a laughter session. Since yogic laughter is a new concept, a proper understanding of the subject is very necessary. Books, literature and instructional videos are available at the headquarters of the Laughter Club International. It is better to go through them before starting a Laughter Club. Being a new concept, people might ask many questions which need to be answered. On behalf of the Laughter Club International we keep holding anchor person training programmes from time to time. For training laughter leaders all over the world we have set up an institution 'Dr. Kataria's School of Laughter Yoga' which will hold training programmes from time to time in various countries. For details about training programmes one can visit our website www.laughteryoga.org.

IMPORTANT : At the time of opening a new Laughter Club, a proper anchor person should be selected. He/she should be very regular and should be able to conduct the session from the very next day. Many clubs do not take off well because of the selection of the wrong anchor person.

HOW TO GIVE A COMMAND

The most important skill of an anchor person in a laughter session is to give commands to participants to initiate different types of laughter and other exercises. The basic purpose of giving a command is to make all the members of the group laugh at the same time. This helps to build up a good tempo of laughter and creates a good effect which stimulates others to laugh. In contrast, if different group members laugh with different tones and timings, it will not elicit a satisfactory response. The response of the group will depend upon the proper commands and energy levels of the leader. Therefore, a leader should always be swift and full of energy. His voice should be audible and clear.

A typical laughter command is given by saying One....Two.... Three or One... Two.... Start... It should be delivered slowly, loudly and building towards a crescendo, that is, with gradually increasing volume. For example you should say one in a normal tone, two should be little louder

The employees of Electrical Products of India (EPI) start their day with laughter.

and t...h....r....eeeeee.... should be said with such gusto that all the members are stimulated to laugh at the same time, which has a good effect. To initiate deep breathing, all the participants should start at the same time because the timing of inspiration, holding the breath and expiration has to be monitored according to yogic principles. So, it is important to have all the members start at the same time. Therefore, to initiate deep breathing the command should be: Now we'll take a deep breath.... Ready.... Start.....! The word 'start' should be said a little louder.

For stretching exercises, the commands are a little different. Normally, we do five rounds of each stretching exercise of the neck and shoulders. First one must name the exercise and then say one..... (slowly).....two.........., three........., four........ and five. Members should be asked to do the exercise slowly and at the end of the range of movement a pleasurable stretch should be maintained and then they come back to the starting position. The anchor person himself should do it slowly to demonstrate the speed of the movement. If necessary, the proper execution of exercises should be demonstrated from time to time for the benefit of new members. Instructing and correcting members during the session should be avoided. It might waste time and may cause embarrassment to the participant.

FORMATTING THE GROUP

Since *Hasya Yoga* (Laughter Yoga) is a dynamic exercise, what is very important, is how to make the group members stand and at what distance from each other. Mostly people prefer to stand in a circle format with the anchor person in the middle. In this format the leader should keep turning around so as to keep eye contact with all the members. If the anchor is not turning in a circle, people standing behind him feel ignored or less motivated. Sometimes introvert and shy members would like to stand behind to evade the public eye. This will create hurdles in removing their inhibitions and in the proper execution of various laughter exercises. Another effective format is a semicircle, where the anchor person stands at one end and maintains eye contact with all the members.

DISTANCE BETWEEN MEMBERS

This distance between members is very important. While doing stretching exercises more distance is needed so that members do not touch each other with stretched arms. But, if the distance between the members is too much it will not allow proper eye contact between participants in order to convert stimulated laughter into genuine giggles. Secondly, while laughing one should not be self-conscious about maintaining a distance from others. Look into another member's eyes and laugh. Then one should move on to other members to share the laugh.

Therefore, according to the new model of a laughter therapy session, all the exercises along with deep breathing are done at the beginning of the session. This also allows more and more members who are a few minutes late to join in. Also, stretching exercises make participants more relaxed and less inhibited to do laughing exercises. Therefore, it is allright to maintain a distance between members initially, while doing exercises, but when starting with the first laughter exercise, the anchor should call all the members a little closer. Try to make it like a random group. There is no need to stand in a queue during a laughter session. In fact, members should be instructed to keep moving and changing their places, going up to different members and laughing with them. Standing steady in one particular place is a sign of inhibition and rigidity, which will affect the quality of laughter. The varying distances and movements will help to bring in more playfulness, which in turn will help to make the laughter session more spontaneous and enjoyable.

At the end of the session, the group members are asked to come still closer to do gradient laughter and to shout the laughter slogans. Gradient laughter is a most enjoyable and powerful type of laughter. It is much closer to spontaneous and meditative laughter. It can only be performed well if members are asked to come closer.

MOTIVATION LEVELS

To make people laugh without jokes is no laughing matter. It needs both skill and motivation levels to make a laughter session truly enjoyable. In addition to giving proper commands, the anchor person should be a good motivator. He should be able to inspire others to keep their spirits high. Therefore, the anchor person himself should be dynamic and full of energy. To keep spirits high one should remember the philosophy of 'Motion creates Emotion'. If you act like an energetic man you will become one over a period of time. With the repetitive actions of acting happy and energetic, it will become a part of your nature after sometime. Therefore, just as charity starts from home, likewise to motivate others, get motivated yourself first.

To motivate others, the anchor person should move around in the circle going up to different members and making hand gestures as if saying "Come on", "Come out". Also he should verbalise encouraging words like "Wonderful", "Very good", "First Class" etc. In between the laughter exercises he must say, "Relax! Relax!" to make people more comfortable. Lastly, to keep the self-interest motive intact, there must be continual innovations and introducing of new items as per the recommendations of our central research team. One should be open to introducing new things in place of less interesting old actions. Therefore, the anchors should stay in touch with the Laughter Club International headquarters through correspondence, telephone, fax, e-mail etc.

DISCIPLINE IN A LAUGHTER CLUB

One of the features of a successful anchor person is being able to maintain discipline about timings and duration of laughter sessions. The entire session should be short and sweet, not lasting for more than 20-25 minutes. One of the hallmarks of a Laughter Club is that it starts sharp on time. Even if there are very few people the clapping and Ho Ho Ha Ha must start without waiting for other members to arrive. Now, people set their watches at the onset of a laughter session. There are many reasons for this punctuality, one of them being that many members have to go to work. The anchor person can't afford to be late and he has to reach five minutes earlier than the scheduled time of a laughter session.

The word discipline does not mean regimentation or bossing. One of the beauties of a Laughter Club is that there are no compulsions or strict rules that one has to come everyday, or one has to reach on time. It is up to the member to decide whether he wants to come everyday, or twice a week, or occasionally as and when he wishes to do so. But if the laughter session is being introduced by an organisation then their rules have to be followed. Normally, in public parks we leave it entirely up to the members' discretion as to how many times they want to attend. Our simple logic is, if the sessions are good and enjoyable why should people miss them?

The idea of maintaining discipline is to maintain orderliness, togetherness and harmony. We favour administration with love and not with force. Even if some member tries to disturb the harmony of the club he should be gently spoken to after the session is over. The anchor should avoid scolding or shouting at him in front of everybody during the session. Inspite of the best efforts, if some member hampers the smooth functioning of the club, the anchor is fully authorised to ban the offender's entry, not by law but by the consensus of the existing members of the group.

TRAINING CO-ANCHORS

Laughter must go on 30 days in a month, 365 days in a year. In case the main anchor is not available, there should be a couple of co-anchors who

Laughter meditation in progress during one of the training workshops held in Paris

should be able to run the show effectively. In my experience, the best leaders are those who glorify others and get their recognition. Some anchors have the tendency to lead the show all by themselves, not allowing others to come forward and conduct the session.

If you find that new anchors are able to conduct the whole session effectively, start slowly by asking them to conduct exercises and deep breathing first and then go on to different laughter exercises. Another good idea is to conduct the entire session jointly by dividing various sets of laughter commands. And by doing so, you can always ask new people to come forward and start by giving one particular command first.

This will create very good harmony among the members and help more and more people achieve self-confidence. The Laughter Club of Mulund has created more than 30 anchors in a group of 80-100 members. More and more women should be encouraged to anchor the proceedings. This will remove stage fright and fear of public speaking and develop self-confidence. Allowing others to be anchors will help them to transform their personalities from introverts to extroverts. There are hundreds of such examples in Laughter Clubs, where some people who could not speak even a word in public earlier, now effectively anchor laughter sessions.

KEEP RELIGION AND POLITICS AWAY

We are dreaming of a unified world and of bringing about world peace through Laughter. On the basis of any religion we can never unite the world and bring communal harmony. Laughter belongs to everyone and it has the potential to become a common link between people of all religions, castes, creeds, colours, the rich and poor, boss and subordinate. Different religions may help to achieve spiritual enlightenment through different religious practices, but laughter is one of the easiest and most acceptable forms of spirituality. We are taking the best of the wisdom from all religions and implementing it practically in Laughter Clubs to achieve health and happiness.

Laughter sessions are held early in the morning and that is the time people go to religious places and say prayers. In Laughter Clubs due to the beliefs of anchor persons, some prayers and chanting of religious hymns were introduced. Though it was liked by many members, this was harming the secular format of Laughter Clubs. This platform is open to all communities. However broad-minded a person may be, still you can't make him accept anything based on a particular religion. Prayers might not elicit the same devotion in the mind of a person belonging to another religion. Therefore, it is the duty of an anchor person not to undertake any prayers or let anybody belonging to a particular religion take advantage of Laughter Clubs. In many clubs which had already started prayers I had to put in very hard efforts to convince them to stop. I told them, prayer is a very personal thing and it should be done in a private place or a religious institution. Prayers are never said casually in a public place. I further told them that religion had always divided people and had sparked off communal violence all over the world.

ORGANISING FUN GAMES, PICNICS, HEALTH CAMPS

In addition to laughter sessions in the mornings, most clubs are now organising outings, picnics and health camps. The expenses involved in these activities can be contributory. Family members, friends and relatives of regular member may be invited for such occasions. This is one way of marketing laughter and increasing the membership of your club. If the gatherings on such occasions are good, you can approach local banks, popular stores, companies or business houses to sponsor such events by putting up their banners to cover a part of the expenses.

ASSIST IN RESEARCH

From time to time we will be conducting medical research to evaluate the health benefits of laughter therapy. Anchor persons can help the research team in interviewing club members and getting the research proforma filled in. Even if some tests are be conducted, they will be entirely sponsored by the central body, the Laughter Club International.

IMPORTANT ANNOUNCEMENTS

The anchor person will act as a bridge between club members and the Laughter Club International. From time to time we will keep sending mailers about various activities, research findings, new developments and different projects to bring good health and happiness to members. We will also send information about various national and international conferences on laughter and humour. With the help of behaviour scientists from all over the world, we will help Laughter Club members to overcome negative emotions like fear, anger, guilt, jealousy etc. At present we have designated Monday as 'Compliment Day' and Friday as 'Forgiveness Day' to help members bring about inner happiness. Anchor persons will keep making announcements to implement these programmes. If necessary, copies can be made and distributed among the members.

HEALTH WATCH

Anchors will keep a watch on various club members asking them about their welfare from time to time. Once a fortnight, an announcement should be made to inform the members about who should not participate in laughter sessions. For example, any one having angina problem (chest pain), hernia, glaucoma, cough with sputum for more than 10 days, acute viral infections (cold, flu), uterovaginal prolapse and slipped disc prob-

Birmingham Laughter Club, UK.

lems with back pain, should consult their doctors before attending a laughter session. If any person feels any discomfort during a session he should consult his doctor before joining the next session. Any elderly person with complaints of giddiness should get himself checked by his doctor. For hygienic reasons, a pack of tissues should be kept in case someone gets phlegm while laughing. Members should be discouraged from spitting in the open. Anchors will also keep a watch on those members who are over-exerting during the session.

IRREGULARITIES AND CHANGE OF FORMAT

With the growing popularity of the laughter movement, many groups have started laughter sessions on their own, without proper training. This might cause some harm as the sessions should be monitored by medical experts. We also encourage the clubs to keep experimenting with new ideas to create playfulness and fun in Laughter Clubs. But some leaders try to change the existing laughter exercises according to their own judgement. If the main exercises are not standardised, it becomes difficult to do medical research to evaluate which particular exercise is more beneficial and which is less so. It has also been observed that according to the liking of some anchors, various types of new exercises are introduced which significantly reduce the duration of laughter exercises, as the total duration of the whole session is 20-25 minutes.

If a particular group wants to introduce more exercises or other items, they should be done before the scheduled time or after the laughter session is over. Extra exercises should not be a compulsion for all the members. If certain types of laughter or exercises are liked by a particular group other than the standard format, they should not exceed 5 minutes.

WELCOME NEW MEMBERS

It is a tradition in many clubs to call first-time visitors into the center and give them welcome laughter. Similarly, if a member of any other club from the same city or from outstation happens to visit your club, he must be acknowledged and honoured. This will motivate many new members to join your club.

ATTENDING SEMINARS AND CONFERENCES

Periodically we will hold seminars and conferences to share new ideas from experts on laughter and humour and behaviour scientists from around the world. The leaders and co-anchors must attend these sessions to gain new insights and implement innovative concepts. During health workshops and yoga and meditation camps, anchor persons must take the opportunity to call a few members forward to share their experiences with Laughter Therapy.

HEALTH CAUTIONS FOR ANCHOR PERSONS

One of most important precautions every leader must take is not to overstrain the voice. In order to motivate the group members, leaders have to make extra efforts which can sometimes put an unnecessary strain on the body. Most vulnerable are the vocal cords which may develop nodules, which may lead to permanent hoarseness. Utmost care should be taken not to put extra strain on any part of the body while giving demonstrations/commands during laughter sessions.

CHAPTER - 23

World Laughter Day World Peace Through Laughter

Today, we are on the brink of nuclear disaster and wide spread international terrorism. More and more countries are acquiring nuclear capabilities. Having nuclear bombs is not a guarantee of peace, as thought by many top leaders of the world. If one mad man presses the button, others will have to respond. Why is there so much unrest in the world these days?

We are at war within ourselves, that is why there is war outside in the world today. If we can bring peace inside us through Laughter Clubs, by doing yogic laughter and practising ways and means of sensible living in a group and these small groups multiply all over the world, there will be everlasting peace in the entire world. Laughter is a powerful positive emotion. It creates a positive aura around individuals. When a group of individuals laughs together, it creates a collective community aura. Electromagnetic waves from a group who are laughing every day, form a protective envelope around that area to protect it from evil forces. Similarly, people believed in days gone by that one saintly person was enough to protect the entire village. If these laughter groups multiply all over the country it will change the consciousness of the entire nation. Similarly, having Laughter Clubs all over the world can build up a global consciousness of brotherhood and friendship. To spread the message of world peace through Laughter Clubs all over the world we have decided to celebrate World Laughter Day on the second Sunday of every May, when thousands of people would gather to laugh together at a public place or a stadium.

Normally any world event should be so designated by the United Nations to get international support. We thought getting United Nations approval at this stage might be difficult as this is a new organisation and we still have to build up international consensus and prove our bonafides by conducting some more research before the world community accepts it. It was only to bring about more awareness internationally that our central body, the Laughter Club International decided to celebrate the event on the second Sunday of every January. Ideally, we should start the new year with laughter only. But people hardly sleep on the night of December 31st, so it was difficult to have gatherings on the 1st morning. Since the first Sunday might fall too close to 1st January the second Sunday was the best choice. Ultimately, if we are thinking of making it an international event, the month of January is freezing in half of the world. We are thinking of shifting World Laughter Day to the month of April or May when more and more countries can join in and laugh together.

FIRST WORLD LAUGHTER DAY

The 11th day of January, 1998, went down in history, when more than 12,700 members from Laughter Clubs all over India and a few invitees from other countries assembled and laughed together at the race course grounds, in Mahalaxmi, Mumbai, to tell the entire world that we need to take laughter seriously. The enthusiastic participation by thousands of members has proved that these Laughter Clubs are not a laughing matter. The grounds which are usually filled with the sound of horses galloping,

World Laughter Day celebrations in Mumbai.

the groans of many losers and the laughter of a few winners, perhaps for the first time, reverberated with laughter and happiness. To participate in the celebrations, members of various clubs along with their near and dear ones, arrived at Worli Seaface, overlooking the vast expanse of the Arabian Sea. The participants dressed in white, wearing laughter logo caps and holding colourful banners, were bubbling with energy with smiles on their faces. Placards read "World Peace Thru' Laughter", "Join a Laughter Club, It's Free", "I am a Laughter Club Member," etc.

A four-kilometer 'Peace March' was flagged off with chanting of Ho Ho Ha Ha Ha and frequent bouts of voluntary group laughter. It looked as if they could not possibly wait to convey to the world, the message that laughter elevates people's minds, raises their spirits, improves their health, enhances their well being, brings them closer and unites them. Laughter could, therefore, also unite nations and bring about world peace.

HISTORIC LAUGHTER DAY IN COPENHAGEN

Inspired by World Laughter Day celebrations in Mumbai, Jan Thygesen Poulsen, a dynamic young man from Copenhagen, sent me an e-mail expressing his desired to set up a Laughter Club in Denmark and decided to celebrate World Laughter Day in January 2000. Jan created history by gathering nearly 10,000 people in the Town Hall Square on 9th January 2000. Inspite of cold weather these thousands of people turned up and had a laughter session, thereby creating a Guiness Book record.

WORLD LAUGHTER DAY 2001

World Laughter Day has been celebrated on the second Sunday of January every year. Due to popular demand from laughter lovers world over, our central body the Laughter Club International has resolved to designate the 1st Sunday of every May instead of January as World Laughter Day (WLD) because of very cold weather conditions in most western countries in January.

In 2001, World Laughter Day was celebrated all over the world in countries like India, USA, Germany, Denmark, Norway and Singapore. In Bangalore nearly 2000 members gathered near the High Court building and celebrated the occasion. In Pune, 800 Laughter Club members walked through the streets with banners proclaiming "World Peace through Laughter". Similarly, there were reports of WLD celebrations from Mumbai, Hyderabad, Kolhapur, Nasik and other cities of India.

BARODA (India) : Mr. Keshav Kumar, Superintendent of Police in Baroda (Gujarat), took the initiative of celebrating World Laughter Day with police personnel. This was a historic day for Vadodara Rural Police, because 125 policemen and officers took part in the celebration along with 100 members of local Laughter Clubs. This marked the entry of the Police Department into this unexplored, vibrant and energy charging field. The policemen enjoyed every bit of it.

DENMARK : The largest gathering was in Copenhagen, Denmark where more than 5000 people gathered at Town Hall Square. Dr. Madan Kataria and Madhuri Kataria were the chief guests. A prayer for world peace, a laughter session, musical programme, laughter competition and comedy shows by a famous Danish comedian were highlights the function. The programme was organised by Jan Thygesen Poulsen the President of International Laughter Clubs, Denmark.

New York : World Laughter Day in New York was a great success. It was a perfect Spring day and witnessed a large turnout. About 200 people of all ages and nationalities actually joined in the laughter exercises and prayers for world peace, while hundreds more observed the proceedings carefully from a distance, laughing along sometimes in spite of themselves. Laraaji Narananda played drums and led us all in the Happy Feet song.

Berlin : World Laughter Day was celebrated in Berlin, the German capital, at Alexanderplatz. Inspite of bad weather (6 degrees celcius and an icy cold wind) more than 400 people turned up for the celebrations. There were several celebrities there and the event received national TV and newspaper coverage. All in all, it was a big success.

Call for a Unified World

Through the Laughter Club movement we want to remind the whole world that human beings are the only species blessed by the Almighty with the gift of laughter. Today we have forgotten to laugh and there is an urgent need to take laughter seriously. Laughter is an universal language which has the potential to unite humanity without a particular religion. Laughter is a neo-religion which can establish a common link between various religions and create a new world order. The idea sounds over-ambitious, but these are the vibrations I am getting from the Creator. Yes! It is laughter and only laughter which can unite the world.

Why Not Include Laughter in the Olympics?

On the occasion of the second World Laughter Day, we strongly recommended the introduction of a 'Laughter Contest' during the Olympics. In fact the opening day should start with a laughter session by athletes from all over the world and viewers should join them.

I am willing to give them training. Is anybody listening? The idea of a Laughter Contest at the Olympics was conceived by a young Indian boy in 1995. Just before the Atlanta Olympics, one of three lads who qualified for the Visa Olympics of the Imagination (VOIs) a future Olympic sport was Nirmal John from India. The contest asked children aged between 11

World Laughter Day celebrations in May 2001, in Stuttgart, Germany.

and 13 years to create their own vision of a new Olympic sport and to describe how their new sport would promote world peace and unity. The young Indian proposed that a Laughter Contest should be included in the Olympics, because it would certainly promote world peace.

It would bring down tension among nations and help to attain everlasting peace. Nirmal John's artwork depicted five persons (representing five countries, of different races, including a woman) taking part in a laughter contest.

The Laughter Club International is a non-religious, non-parochial and non-commercial organisation. We are committed to spreading the message of good health, friendship and brotherhood all over the world. In our future plans we are introducing laughter at work places, schools and colleges, during competitive sports, at old age homes, for destitute women's groups, in prisons, orphanages and blind institutes, on ships and for the police, army, navy and air force.

CHAPTER - 24

Research in Laughter Therapy

L aughter is as old as mankind itself and its benefits have been felt for centuries. Everybody understands that laughter is beneficial and relaxing. But, it is only recently that the scientific basis for the benefits of laughter has been established. This chapter analyses the scientific principles of the medical benefits of laughter therapy, on the basis of research work done by many scientists all over the world and some of the clinical data gathered from Laughter Clubs in India.

LAUGHTER AS PRACTISED BY US

Laughter as practised by us is different from laughter therapy practised in the Western world. They have hospital-based laughter clinics for individual patients who are made to laugh by reading jokes or viewing comic videos. Our laughter is unprovoked, spontaneous group laughter by healthy individuals which works as a preventive health measure.

Mr. P. T. Hinduja receiving the 'Best Laughing Man' Award in 1998.

LAUGHTER AS AN EUSTRESS OR STRESS BUSTER

Hans Selye described laughter as a form of Eustress. This means that it is a positive, life enhancing type of stress. Laughter has a built-in balancing mechanism that encourages the two-step action of stimulation and relaxation due to the release of the chemicals adrenaline and noradrenaline. This produces a feeling of well-being by relieving the minor stresses and strains of daily life. Laughter reduces anxiety, tension and depression. Thus, it helps in mitigating several serious diseases such as hypertension, heart disease, diabetes, etc. in which anxiety and tension are predisposing factors. Kay Herth *(American Journal of Nursing 1984)* has documented reduction of hypertension after laughter therapy. Many of our members have reaped the beneficial effects of laughter in reducing hypertension, heart disease, diabetes, anxiety, insomnia, etc.

LAUGHTER AND HEALING

Laughter releases catecholamines together with adrenaline and noradrenaline. This enhances blood flow, reduces inflammation, speeds up the healing process and heightens the overall arousal of the body. Thus it would help in mitigating arthritis, spondylitis, myofascitis and other such inflammatory diseases.

LAUGHTER AS AN ANALGESIC

Laughter releases two neuropeptides viz. Endorphins and Enkephalins. These are opioids, which are the body's natural pain suppressing agents. The ability of laughter to release muscle tension and to soothe the sympathetic nervous system also helps to control pain, as does increased circulation. Thus, laughter has a multipronged approach for the relief of pain, in conditions such as arthritis, spondylitis, etc.

This is aptly demonstrated by the famous article of Norman Cousins *(New England Journal of Medicine,* Dec. 1976) where he documents that 10 minutes of laughter had an analgesic effect for 2 hours in his personal problem of severe ankylosing spondylitis. Cogan et al *(Journal of Behavioural Medicine* 1987) demonstrated by clinical experiments that discomfort thresholds were higher in subjects after bouts of laughter. Some (21%) of our members with painful orthopaedic conditions have obtained relief.

LAUGHTER AND IMMUNITY

Lee S. Berk *(Clinical Research* 1989) found that laughter may attenuate some stress related hormones and modify natural killer cell activity, resulting in immunomodulation. Labott also supports Berk's findings *(Journal of Behavioural Medicine* 1990) and concludes that laughter results in improved immunity. In a study at Canada's University of Waterloo *(Well Being Journal),* it was well documented that laughter increases the levels of immunoglobulin IgA and IgG. Norman Cousins *(Prevention* March 1988) also states that laughter serves as a blocking agent against disease.

Thus laughter, by improving body immunity, can mitigate a host of chronic diseases such as bronchitis, the common cold, rheumatoid arthritis, allergies, etc. Improving immunity may also be a supplementary measure in the control of AIDS. Some (12.9%) of our members recorded improvements in chronic diseases such as bronchitis, common cold, etc.

Lion Laughter has helped many women remove their inhibitions and find their sense of humour.

CANCER AND LAUGHTER

In Berk and Tan's (1996) experiment concerning the laughter immune connection, they used a few healthy fasting males who volunteerred for the experiment and had them view a funny one-hour video film. They took blood samples of their interferon-gamma (IFN) before, during and after they had watched the film. They obtained significant results which showed increased activity in IFN after watching the funny video, which lasted till the following day. IFN activates the CT-Cells, B-Cells immunoglobulins and Natural Killer (NK) Cells.

This could be very important research for cancer, since laughter also fights against tumour cells. Laughter's ability to be a pain reliever and its ability to fight tumour cells have added an exciting new area in cancer research. In our Laughter Clubs there are many cancer patients who are leading much healthier lives due to a positive attitude towards life. This makes us believe that laughter can be used as a preventive measure against cancer.

LAUGHTER AS AN AEROBIC EXERCISE

Dr. W. Fry states that laughter is a good aerobic exercise. He says that 100 laughs a day are equal to 10 minutes of rowing or jogging. Lloyd (*Journal of General Psychology* 1938) showed that laughter is a combination of deep inhalation and full exhalation, inspiring excellent ventilation, wonderful rest and profound release. Thus, laughter increases the lungs' vital capacity and oxygenation. We measured the lungs' vital capacity (peak flow rate) of our members using a Spirometer. The peak flow rate was lower than normal in 13%, (<300l/m.) it was normal in 67% (300-500 l/m.) and high in 20% (>500l/m.). This would benefit patients with pulmonary diseases such as bronchitis, bronchial asthma, bronchiectasis, etc. Some (7.8%) of our members have gained relief from such lung diseases.

LAUGHTER - A HOLISTIC APPROACH

Laughter has positive holistic benefits for normal healthy individuals, such as improved concentration, better performance in examinations (Sobina White 1987), improved stamina in sportsmen and better performance by actors and singers. It increases self-confidence, improves interpersonal relationships and is also a simple method of meditation. All these benefits have been aptly demonstrated by a large majority of our members who are otherwise healthy individuals.

RESEARCH SURVEY IN INDIA

In India laughter has been in use as a therapeutic exercise and research interest has gradually increased, focussing on this aspect. A few survey studies have been conducted by Sheetal Agarwal that highlight the perceived therapeutic effects of laughter therapy.

Due to several limitations, other more sophisticated forms of research such as experimental research have not been conducted. But an adequate consolation is that we are moving towards accumulating more and more scientific evidence that validates the use of laughter as an effective form of therapy. Here are some of the physiological parameters of the research survey.

Parameter	% of Survey Population	% Who Perceive Improvement
Regular Walkers	97.56	86.25
Diabetes	13.4	9
Blood pressure	31.7	26.9
Respiratory problems	17.0	14.2
Heart disease	7.3	33.3
Quality of sleep	57.3	65.8

It is important to note that a significant percentage of people suffering from heart disease perceived betterment after joining Laughter Clubs, especially pertaining to a reduction in chest pains.

PSYCHOLOGICAL MEASURES :

Coping better with anxiety and feelings of depression	19.5%
Coping better with stress	69.5%
Increased social interaction	74.39%
Noticeable change in mood and attitude	79.6%

With reference to psychological measures, the data available suggests a comparatively greater perceived effect. This is very evident in terms of participants of laughter therapy finding themselves coping better with stress. Though it has to be further studied as to how laughter therapy affects the individual's appraisal process in terms of a stressful situation, in a way that enables him to deal with stress more effectively. Also, it will be interesting to study the kinds of stresses for which laughter therapy is found most effective.

The results also suggest an increase in the participants' level of social interaction. This, in more ways than one, provides for the psychological well-being of the individual. Participants of laughter therapy also find a marked change in their moods, as well as an attitudinal change. Finding themselves to be more positive in their outlook is a common experience for many of them, shown as a high percentage i.e. 79.26%, in the study. 98.7% of the participants find the format of laughter therapy adequate in terms of time and the structure of exercises. Hence, it can be concluded that though much more structured procedures of research need to be implemented to assess the effects of laughter therapy, this study is a stepping stone in unravelling the basic effects perceived by the patients.

CLINICAL ANALYSIS OF 516 MEMBERS OF LAUGHTER CLUBS FROM ALL OVER INDIA

This study was conducted by Dr. Siddhartha D. Khandwala, M.D. (Bom.,) who is the anchor person of the Priyadarshani Laughter Club, Mumbai. Most members (71.7%) were males and in the age group of 50 to 70 years (63.5%) and retired individuals or housewives (40.2%), as senior citizens are more interested in such activities. However, almost 10% were younger people. It is necessary to target younger people and students, as well as women.

This movement has started only recently and still almost 40% of its members have been attending it for over a year. It is most heartening to note that 93.8% of members are regular participants, indicating the popularity of laughter sessions. A majority (59.3%) of members suffer from some ailment, as would be expected in this age group. However, it is surprising to note that such simple laughter therapy has resulted in amelioration of the ailment in as many as 83.6%. The amelioration was of a moderate to substantial degree in 56.1%. It was heartening to note that 44% needed less medication and there was not a single case of worsening of the disease.

The holistic benefits of Laughter Therapy are well documented and have recorded a positive improvement in members' general health, both mental and physical. The attitude of a majority (82.6%) of members towards their family members improved, resulting in a more harmonious family life. 71.7% of members reported an improved relationship with their colleagues in their profession, business or place of service. Self-confidence was increased in 85.7%, while 66.7% reported increased concentration.

Almost all (99.6%) stated that they would like to continue laughter sessions as well as recommend the same to others. Many members reported several additional tangible benefits such as feeling energetic and fresh (31.1%); an improved outlook on life (11.2%); improved social behaviour and contacts (8.5%); increased stamina (3.9%); increased appetite and improved digestion (3%). All these minor benefits go towards improving the quality of life.

CONCLUSION

Thus, laughter has several medical/social/holistic benefits which can improve the quality of life substantially. Laughter can help to mitigate several diseases, some of them quite serious. Laughter is a "Stress Buster" and helps to relieve anxiety and tension which are the predisposing factors for several diseases. Laughter every day can keep the doctor away at no cost.

**Laugh Like
a Chinese Emperor**

CHAPTER - 25

Laughter Among Senior Citizens, Prisoners and Disabled Children

O ne of the universal laws is that whatever is born will die one day. Almost every one of us will go through old age. Due to advancements in medical science the average age is going up and according to some estimates in the next 30-40 years the number of older people will outnumber the younger people, especially in developed countries. Due to immense stress and strain during one's younger days, the body starts showing sign of wear and tear once you cross the age of 60. Many older people live in old age homes and feel very lonely and depressed. I have visited many such places and found that they don't laugh and smile much. Suicide rates among the elderly are also high. Though they live with other elderly people and there is community feeling, they miss their children and family members very much. They feel very happy when someone visits them. At this age, all they need is to talk to someone and friends to share their emotions. I believe laughter can provide them with the much needed sense of fellowship and connectedness. As we get older, our capacity to laugh keeps going down. Laughter exercises can help older people to keep their spirits high and help them come out of depression. In India, a majority of Laughter Club members are over the age of 50-60. They are significantly benefited from Laughter Clubs. In addition to physical exercise, these clubs have helped them to find much needed social support. This is very good for their physical, mental and emotional well-being.

Aerobic Exercise

Laughter is also equivalent to aerobic exercise in terms of cardio-pulmonary endurance. According to Prof. William Fry, 10 minutes of laughter is equivalent to half-an-hour on a rowing machine. In other words, laughter provides exercise to the lungs and circulatory system to push the heart rate up to a level comparable to any aerobic exercise. This fact is very important for older people who cannot walk and do not do much physical exercise because of weak muscles and arthritis problems. Therefore, laughter is an ideal workout for those who have physical limitations.

Elderly people also suffer from aches and pains in the joints and there is muscular stiffness. Laughter triggers the release of endorphins which act as pain killers. Many elderly people who previously had difficulty in sleeping and needed tranquillisers and sleeping pills, found laughter yoga exercises helpful in getting better quality sleep and many of them stopped needing sleeping pills.

One of the most profound effects of laughter is on depression. This may be due to biochemical changes occurring within the body and also due to the social contacts depressed people get from Laughter Clubs members. Laughter Club activities have helped them to became more playful and celebrative.

The Danish Experience

I visited many old age homes in many countries but had a unique experience in Copenhagen, Denmark. I was invited to laugh with a group of 70 residents of a senior citizen's home. More than 10 elderly persons were on wheel chairs and could not move much. After the initial briefing we started with the laughter session and we took all the persons who were on wheelchairs into the center and we laughed with them. We greeted them with laughter, shook hands with them and played with them. Everyone had a good laughter session, except those on wheelchairs who were not participating much and we thought they may not have liked the idea. To our surprise when we spoke to them after the session they told us that although they were not able to laugh much they loved being touched and greeted with laughter. They were keenly looking forward to more sessions like this on a regular basis. Many laughter leaders go to senior citizens' homes to cheer them up as a part of their social commitment.

Steve Wilson told me that many laughter leaders in US have tried laughter sessions with older people and found them very useful. Steve Wilson wrote in his article about the role of Laughter Clubs that they contribute their potential power as a therapeutic activity among older people. Here are some of the highlights of such sessions:

❖ They are adaptable to all levels and limitations of cognitive, sensory, and motor ability.

❖ They do not require any ability to tell jokes or perform humourously.

❖ They provide physical exercise that involves large and small muscles, and strengthens breathing ability.

❖ They reduce suffering and contribute to the restoration of optimal health and independence.

❖ They take place in a socially supportive group setting.

❖ They transcend most linguistic barriers.

❖ They encourage healthy attitudes and peace of mind, such as through paying compliments and being less angry.

❖ They are not passive-receptive, but adapt to all levels of capacity for interaction.

❖ They are an inviting, not demanding, activity.

❖ They provide a simple, structured, playful routine that is based on sound scientific principles.

❖ They lift the spirits of staff and residents alike.

❖ There is some early indication that families prefer placing elder members in facilities that provide Laughter Club programming.

LAUGHTER AMONG POLICE PERSONNEL

It seems that the simple idea of a Laughter Club has many applications and it is constantly evolving. With increasing crime, police personnel are under stress and the police department in India keeps organising different methods of stress release like yoga meditation. During my travels to spread Laughter Clubs, I was invited to conduct a seminar by the police academy in Nasik and Baroda. In the beginning it was very difficult to make policemen laugh in front of their senior officers, but once they started laughing the ice was broken and the laughing session worked well. Initially, it was also hard for policemen to laugh because looking serious and tough is part of their job description. I could see the visible relaxation on their faces after the session. A senior police officer in Baroda (Gujarat) Mr. Keshav Kumar took the initiative of introducing laughter therapy among police officers before the allocation of their duties in the morning. It has also been introduced in the police academy in Ahmedabad as a part of their training drill once a week.

LAUGHTER AMONG PRISONERS

Two years ago, John Cleese, the famous English actor, came to Mumbai to make a documentary film titled "Human Face" and the Laughter Clubs of India was the part of the series. During John's visit I took him to many Laughter Clubs, factories and finally to Arthur Road prison for a laughter session. Laughter among prisoners was a humbling experience. I obtained permission to hold a laughter session among undertrials from the police authorities. One hour before the laughter session I went into the overcrowded prison premises to build a rapport with them and asked if they would like to laugh with me. I explained the concept to them and 70-80 prisoners opted to join the laughter session.

I was not too sure whether they would laugh or not because they looked very sad, angry and depressed. Some of them had mask-like faces. Along with my laughter leaders, I started with different laughter exercises and after initial hesitation they opened up and laughed uproariously, as if all their anger was transformed into laughter. At the end of the session, everybody seemed happy and asked when they would laugh like this again. Some of the police officers who were watching the proceedings asked me to hold a laughter session for police officers too as they also face stress.

I spoke to many prisoners after the laughter session and I could feel that they had a lot of anger and depression. If these negative emotions are not removed, they will resort to crime again when they are released from jail. Now, I have written to the Home Ministry to ask for permission to hold regular laughter sessions among long-term convicted prisoners. I remember having trained a young man from Chicago, USA who was working with prisoners and he too was optimistic about a laughter project in prison.

Laughter can certainly help in resolving the negative emotions in criminals and putting them into a positive frame of mind. This is my dream project and I am sure I will soon gain permission for such an initiative in India and the day is not far off when this idea will be implemented worldwide.

MENTALLY AND PHYSICALLY DISABLED

The city of Bangalore also known as Silicon Valley of India, has the distinction of having more than 70 Laughter Clubs. One of these Laughter Clubs is at the institute for mentally and physically disabled children. One of the teachers there named Mythali, is a Laughter Club member. One day she tried out a laughter session with disabled children and found them more cheerful throughout the day.

From that day onwards she introduced laughter yoga exercise into their curriculum. Their physiotherapist told us that many children who did not respond to their commands earlier, responded spontaneously now and they do their exercises with great interest. This has helped improved their physical and mental well-being. In Perth, Australia I had a similar experience when I conducted a laughter session with physically and mentally disabled children.

CHAPTER - 26

Special Projects in Laughter Clubs

PROJECT "PHONE A FRIEND" (LEARNING THROUGH LAUGHTER)

From 1st September 2001 to 10th October 2001 (40 days), laughter lovers all over the world, participated in a unique project "Phone a Friend" to re-establish connections with those who used to be very close and made some difference to their lives, but due to various reasons had lost touch. An appeal was sent out to Laughter Club members to call up their near and dear ones to say hello and ask about their welfare. The idea was to express love and gratitude and to remind them that the old good days were not forgotten.

GUIDELINES FOR PROJECT "PHONE A FRIEND"

Scan through your memory, old telephone diaries and visiting cards and look for your loved ones under the following categories.

a). Your present friends, colleagues and acquaintances to whom you have not talked for months together.

b). People from the localities where you used to live earlier in the same city as well as in other cities and in other countries. Call up your old business colleagues, friends from previous jobs and from old neighbourhoods.

c). Your childhood friends, school mates, college friends, school teachers, professors and your well wishers. It might be a big challenge to find the contact members of those whose whereabouts are not known to you. For example I found a school teacher of mine with great difficulty but the experience was humbling. She cried for joy. I can't explain my feelings about what such a phone call can do to the heart!

d). Anyone you know who is very old and lonely, people from lower socio-economic strata who have served you and worked for you. If phone numbers are not available, please write a postcard or letter.

THE PHILOSOPHY

UNCONDITIONAL LOVE : There is a normal human tendency of "Out of Sight - Out of Mind" but we laughter lovers will not let this happen. The purpose behind the "Phone a Friend" project is to find the deeper meaning of Laughter, that is, the Spirit of Laughter, which says - Laughter is not all about making oneself happy but making others happy too. Our objective is to develop unconditional love for others without any selfish motive. Most of our actions are directed towards an I, MY, ME agenda that leads to EGOISM, which the basic cause of unhappiness. "Phone a Friend" is one step forward to look beyond oneself and open one's heart to those who might need love and compassion. Remember, one phone call might give someone a moment of joy and lift his or her spirits from despair. We have already conducted trial studies in Mumbai, India. It was a humbling and soul-nourishing experience. Many cried for joy and surprise, while others grieved to find that their loved ones were no more in this world.

40-DAY FORMULA

The philosophy behind the 40-day formula is that any pursuit or good deed repeated 40 times, becomes ingrained. Otherwise it is likely to be forgotten or remains mere knowledge. It does not become manifest in your life. This will further strengthen our belief that anything which is done as a group efforts is manifested with greater ease. There are so many virtues we wish to implement in our lives but this doesn't happen for lack of persistent effort at an individual level. Repetition of any act becomes easy if undertaken in a group because each one keeps motivating the others. A Laughter Club is an excellent platform for GROUP LEARNING. Let us All Unite and Get Happy - that the real meaning of LAUGH.

"Neighbours Day" - July 1, Every Year

We, the Laughter Club members, have found a new meaning of laughter, which is known as the "Spirit of Laughter". Laughter is not just amusement and entertainment, nor it is only giggling and chuckling - it is the way in which we relate to others and how we react to the behaviour and attitude of others. Yet another brilliant idea came from my friend B.K. Satyanarayan, the founder of the Bangalore Laughter Clubs (India). Every year, the first day of July is celebrated as "Neighbours' Day". On this occasion Laughter Clubs members all over the world invite their immediate next door neighbours or any one staying in their neighbourhoods for a cup of tea/coffee, lunch, dinner or outing, depending upon mutual convenience, to show solidarity and commitment towards improving neighbourly relationships.

The Philosophy

Much of our laughter and happiness depends upon the relationships we have with people around us, like our friends, relatives and especially neighbours. Your neighbours can play an important role in the well-being of your family, as they are available 24 hours next door. Friends and relatives may take a while to reach you in an emergency.

A friendly and positive neighbour can enhance one's sense of security and family well-being, while a hostile and negative neighbour can be a source of stress, emotional turbulence, anger, irritation, jealousy and criticism. Let us make a new beginning and make a commitment to establish and nurture this beautiful relationship based on mutual need. Keep the following points in mind while dealing with your neighbours.

1. We need their help and moral support in an hour of emergency like a fire, mishap, theft, robbery, gas leakage, medical emergency or death in the family.

2. We need their help for looking after old parents, children, pets or plants, while we are away for a few hours or even for a few days, of course on mutual understanding.

3. We need their assistance during ceremonies like marriages, birthdays, religious and social functions.

4. We need to share our moments of success and achievement.

5. They help receive or re-direct important letters and documents when one is away for a long time or changes one's house or office.

How to Build up a Rapport with Your Neighbours

1. Always be ready to help your neighbour as your help is like an insurance for you to get your neighbour's help and support when you are in need.

2. Remember the birthdays of your neighbours, especially their children, and also their wedding anniversaries. Make it a point to greet them personally. Send them flowers or a greeting card.

3. Periodically send small gifts or sweets to make them feel special.

4. Be liberal in paying compliments about their houses, their children, their successes and their achievements.

5. Express gratitude even if they do you a small favour.

6. Deliver letters and documents promptly, when wrongly delivered at your address.

7. Be careful about playing loud music during parties and celebrations. If possible make them a part of the festivity and they won't complain.

8. Avoid littering in a common passage and open places that might cause inconvenience to your neighbours.

9. Children, when they play together in a neighbourhood, can create a strong bond between the families and at the same time can create misunderstandings when they fight. So, be careful and compassionate when handling fights among children. Give suggestions and avoid blaming.

CHAPTER - 27

How Can You Start a Laughter Club in Your Area?

LAUGHTER CLUB INTERNATIONAL: The Laughter Club International (LCI) is a worldwide organisation, registered under the Societies Registration Act 1860. It also has a Public Trust exemption from tax under section 80G. It is non-political, non-religious, non-profit organisation.

AIMS AND OBJECTIVES

❖ Our aim is to create awareness of this new yogic technique of Laughter Therapy all over India and other parts of the world, by setting up more Laughter Clubs and imparting practical training in various techniques of laughter. Thus, we can help to cultivate the Spirit of Laughter by understanding ways and means of sensible living and putting them into practice through laughter.

❖ Our aim is to set up a team of doctors from various specialities and systems of medicine to conduct scientific studies and research work as to how laughter can affect the physical, mental, social and spiritual well being of the participants.

❖ Our aim is to publish journals and set up libraries of books, video cassettes, CDs and other information on Laughter Therapy.

❖ Our aim is to bring people of various countries together and promote everlasting peace through laughter.

IN INDIA

SEARCH FOR THE RIGHT PLACE : In India most Laughter Clubs function on an everyday basis and the members meet at public parks where people go for a morning walk. If you want to start a Laughter Club, find a place in your locality where people can assemble early in the morning when they go for a walk. It can be either a public park, an open ground, or a beach. The advantage of selecting such a place is that you can combine laughter therapy sessions with your morning walk. The chosen place should not be in the immediate vicinity of residential complexes so as to prevent any disturbance to others. In areas where weather conditions are not favourable throughout the year, it is not possible to have laughter sessions round the year. Under such circumstances these sessions can be held during yoga classes, at health clubs or at aerobic centres, where laughter can be a value addition to the ongoing activities.

REGISTRATION OF YOUR CLUB : Registration of a laughter club is FREE all over the world. You can download or fill up a form online from our website **www.laughteryoga.org**. Affiliation to Laughter Club International costs Rs.1000/- in India and 25 USD in other countries. The benefits of affiliation you can find at the end of this chapter.

In India to start a social Laughter Club you need to form an Organising Committee consisting of 5 members who will be founder members and will be trained as anchor persons. Include one or two women if possible. After acknowledgment of the registration, organise a group of at least 25-30 people (the larger the better) who would be participating in laughter sessions everyday. We will fix a date for the opening of the Laughter Club in your city. The Laughter Club International will organise a team

One of the outstanding features of the Laughter Clubs in India is that they are very punctual about time. People set their watches by Laughter Clubs!

of experts who will come to your area for a lecture and demonstration of various techniques of yogic laughter. They will also train your anchor persons who will be conducting laughter sessions everyday. The expenses for conveyance, boarding and lodging of the team of experts will be borne by the organising group. If you can't afford the expenses of the team, you can approach social organisations like the Rotary or Lions, or corporate houses and philanthropists to sponsor the event in the public interest. From time to time the Laughter Club International and Dr. Kataria's School of Laughter Yoga keep organising anchor person training programmes all over the world. For training schedules you can keep checking at our website www.laughteryoga.org

LAUGHTER YOGA IN THE WORKPLACE : There are many people who can't get up early in the morning and others who have to rush to their workplaces. They may not be able to attend laughter sessions. The ideal alternative for such people would be to have laughter sessions at their offices, or factories, provided the management is convinced about the benefits of the concept.

IN WESTERN COUNTRIES : The concept of Laughter Clubs is slightly different in Western countries where club members like to meet for 2 hours every weekend or fortnightly. They laugh together for 30 minutes along with breathing and stretching exercises, followed by laughter meditation for another 30 minutes. After that there are humour activities, fun games, brain storming on psychological and philosophical aspects of laughter and dancing with music. This is known as a social Laughter Club. It operates on a no profit basis and all the expenses of the venue, food and drinks are shared by the members. The frequency of such laughter meetings can be increased or decreased according to the convenience of the group.

You need to be trained as a laughter leader to start a laughter club. We organise workshops and training programmes from time to time in Europe, America and Canada. By training yourself as a laughter leader you can do laughter seminars for companies and corporations on stress management through laughter and humour. Also, laughter yoga concept can be value added to those who are professional speakers, motivational speakers and trainers.

AFFILIATION TO THE LAUGHTER CLUB INTERNATIONAL : By affiliation to Laughter Club International you can be a part of the international network of laughter leaders. You are entitled to participate in national and international conferences at reduced price. Also, you can take part in inter club exchange programme where the laughter club members from one country can visit other countries on mutual basis. You will get free hospitality. Also, you will get updates about happenings around the world about laughter movement.

CHAPTER - 28

Laughter Workshops and Laughter Leader Training Programmes

S ince we started the Laughter Clubs initiative there has been an ever increasing demand for opening more Laughter Clubs the world over. I get letters, faxes and e-mails inviting me to conduct workshops and training programmes in different parts of the world. Since this a new concept of group laughter without reason, it requires a basic understanding of the philosophy and the acquiring of skills to learn different stimulated kinds of laughter. We need an anchor person (a laughter leader) who leads the group of people through different laughter yoga exercises along with yogic breathing. Most importantly, such leaders need to learn the right skills to conduct laughter meditation. Also, there are many exercises on child-like playfulness, gibberish talking and humour active techniques which are taught in our workshops.

DURATION OF SEMINARS AND WORKSHOPS

Public awareness seminars are of 1-2 hours duration and provide basic understanding of the laughter yoga concept, along with one laughter session experience. This type of seminar can be organised just before the weekend two-day laughter workshop, which is usually organised on Saturdays and Sundays. The objective of short seminars is to enhance public awareness about the concept as well as to provide access to the media for reporting such activities in newspapers, magazines and over television networks.

WEEKEND CERTIFIED LAUGHTER WORKSHOPS

These are experiential programmes for those who want to add more laughter to their lives, even if they don't have a sense of humour. They also serve to provide a basic understanding for those who wish to start their own Laughter Clubs and act as laughter leaders or fecilitators. These training programmes are conducted by me 2-3 times a year in Germany, Denmark, Sweden, Norway, Switzerland, UK, Italy, France, Hungary, the Middle East, Singapore and Malaysia.

WHAT WILL YOU LEARN: During this course, you will learn the skills of conducting various stimulated laughter exercises developed in India (video presentation) and about LAUGHTER MEDITATION along with 5 powerful, easy meditation methods. Also covered is why we need to laugh more today, scientific research on laughter and its effects on human physiology, biochemistry and behaviour, essential link between yoga and laughter, health benefits of laughter therapy - physical, mental, social and spiritual - how to create a therapeutic laughter group at the workplace and the inner spirit of laughter. How paying compliments and forgiveness, two effective tools of sensible living, help to create harmonious relationship, is another topic covered.

ANGER WORKSHOP : This covers understanding anger - the most common negative emotion: from where does it come? Types of anger - when you get angry with someone and someone gets angry with you; How does anger kill?; Misplaced anger; to express or not to express anger; Difference between SHOWING ANGER and GETTING ANGRY; Justified positive anger to motivate people; dealing with free floating hostilities (irritations) of daily life; the role of laughter and humour to diffuse anger; reframing your thoughts to diffuse anger (shifting attitude); difference between REACTION and RESPONSE; learning the art of FORGIVENESS to control anger (double benefit technique); Resolving Conflict (80-20 formula); Understanding EGO - the seat of anger (EGO busting breathing exercise); and the role of food and exercise to prevent anger.

WHO SHOULD ATTEND?

Anyone who wants to add more laughter, humour and fun to their lives and those who would like to start a Laughter Club. Among them could be Alternative Therapists, Recreation, Activity and Occupational Therapists, Nurses, Social Workers, Counsellors, Health Care Workers and Professional Speakers.

SEVEN-DAY TEACHERS TRAINING PROGRAMME IN INDIA

This is an advanced course to train the laughter yoga teachers who can run their own courses to train laughter leaders. The details of which you can find on our website www.laughteryoga.org. This course is very exhaustive and touches upon the spiritual depths of laughter along with physical training. During the training we organise visits to different Laughter Clubs in parks, factories and blind schools in India.

If you wish to organise such workshops or training programmes please contact us at the following address:

Dr. Kataria's School of Laughter Yoga
Headquarters: A-1, Denzil, 3rd Cross Road,
Lokhandwala Complex, Andheri (W), Mumbai-400 053. (India).
Tel: 022-2631 6426 / Fax: 022-2632 0945,
Email: laugh@laughteryoga.org Website: www.laughteryoga.org

Laugh Like an Egyptian

Laughter Clubs in Major Cities of India

MUMBAI

Mr. B.P. Hirani
**Jogger's Park Laughter Club,
Bandra (W)**
Tel: 022-26558844/26558811

Subhash Khambhati
Laughter Club of Juhu Beach
Tel (R): 2621 2551/26211450
Tel (O): 2206 1124/2206 7375

Mr. G.P. Shethia
Laughter Club of Hanging Garden
Tel:56057767(R), 56359977(O)

Mr. Mohit Kapoor
Worli Seaface Laughter Club
Tel: 2422 8895

Girdhar Peshawaria,
Laughter Club of Gateway of India
Tel: 2284 0238

PUNE

Mr. V. L. Kate
Laughter Club of Pune
Tel: 020-2445 3356

NASIK

S. R. Jain
Anand Hasya Club
Tel:2461977

AHMEDNAGAR

Indrabhan G Bhandari,
Laughter Club of Suprabhat
Tel(O): 2343 540 (R) 2344529

NAGPUR

Kishore Thutheja
Eastern Sport Club
Tel: 2768510, 2773390

KOLHAPUR

Adv. Shri. Arvind C. Shah,
Ruikar Colony Hasya Yoga Club
Tel: 0231-537717/536816
E-mail : kpr_shah@sancharnet.in

Dr. D.C. Shah
Trymboli Hasya-yog Club
Tel:2653545(Clinic), 2659055(R)

AHMEDABAD

Mahendra C Shah
Ahmedabad Laughter Clubs
Tel: 2661 15 16
E-mail: chitrakunj@hotmail.com

SURAT

Mr. Kamlesh I Masalawala
Kavi Kalapi Laughing Club
Tel: 2424611 (R) 2456486 (S)
Mob:9825177601

GANDHINAGAR

Prof . Ravinder J Dave
Laughter Club of Gandhi Nagar
Tel: (02712) 26755

BARODA

Prof. R. P. Gupta
Laughter Clubs of Baroda
Tel: 0265-431170

Pradeep Parikh
Sardar Baug Laughing Club
Tel:0265-398032(R),337071(O)

KOLKATA & WEST BENGAL

Mr. L.N. Daga
Safari Park Laughing Club
Tel: 033-2464 2172 / 1487

S.K. Mall
Kolkatta Laughter Clubs
Tel:22699730/22687572
Res:23597278

HYDERABAD

Shirin Panjwani,
ABC Laughing Club
Tel.: 2475 5000 / 2475 4537

INDORE

S.K. Matlani
Indore Hasya Yog Maha Sangh
Tel: 2466456/457/458

RAIPUR

Mr. Mukund Rathod
Hasya Yoga Centre
Tel:(0771)2228688,2630948

BILASPUR

Dr. I.D. Kalwani
Laughter Club of Bilaspur
Tel: 230870, 269714

BANGALORE

Mr. Satyanarayan - IRSE
Laughter Clubs of Bangalore
Tel: 080-2656 3968 (Res)
E-mail: bsm@bgl.vsnl.net.in

HUBLI

Mr. K. R. Vaishyar
**Hudha Nagu Ogguta
Laughter Club**
Tel: 0836 - 2247691

CHENNAI

Mr. Gautam Khariwal
Laughter Club of Marina Beach
Tel: 26428849, 26481002
Mobile: 98410-63102
E-mail: khariwals@eth.net

NEW DELHI

Dr. Umesh Sahgal
North Delhi Laughter Club
Tel:(011)27217164,27455657

Mr. R.C.Gupta
Laughter Club of Noida
Tel: 91-4582254, 91-4582715

(For complete list of Laughter
Club in India, visit
www.laughteryoga.org)

International Laughter Clubs

NORTH AMERICAN LAUGHTER CLUBS

Steve Wilson
Tel: 614-855-4883
Fax:614-855-4889

Laughaway
Arya Pathria
Tel/Fax: (408)-926-3307
E-mail: laughaway@yahoo.com
www.laughaway.com

CONNECTICUT (Newington),
Lila Wachtel, JLC Laughter Clubs
Tel: 860-667-2377

FLORIDA (Naples)
Barbara
E-mail:<bjt_2002@yahoo.com>

INDIANAPOLIS, Indiana
Rochelle Cohen,
e-mail : RCohen@indy.net
Tel: 317-263-6272

GREENFIELD, Massachusetts
The Laughin' Laugh-In Club
Chairperson: Violet Walker,
<violet_walker@shaysnet.com>

NEW YORK CITY
Vishwa Prakash
Tel: 201 854 6092
E-mail: vishwa@soimex.com
Dr. Alex
E-mail: AEingorn@aol.com

ORRVILLE, Ohio
Jenni Reusser,
<jjjreusser@aol.com>

MEMPHIS, Tennessee
Memphis Cancer Foundation Club
Pat McRee/Jan Harvey
e-mail: <mcree9@msn.com>
Tel: 901-682-3916

FALLS CHURCH, Virginia,
Rebecca Colegrove,
E-mail: <drehj@worldnet.att.net>

CANADIAN LAUGHTER CLUBS

Quebec & Montreal

Club de Rire international du Québec
Contact : Michel Abitbol
Tel: 514-733-2402
Fax: 514-733-3096
E-mail :
michel@clubderirequebec.com
www.clubderirequebec.com

ONTARIO

Orangeville
Jan and Dave MacQuarrie,
Tel:519-942-0860
(Fax: 519-942-5988
519-939-4037 Cell)
E-mail: jan@aplacetwobe.com
www.aplacetwobe.com,

Toronto
Shiv Sud
E-mail: shiv.sud@sympatico.ca

Vancouver
Allan O'Meara
E-mail: humorbeing@shaw.ca

Okanagan
Carole Fawcett
E-mail: flower1@shaw.ca

Yellowknife
Lone Sorensen
E-mail:
<glowing@borealis-coop.nt.ca>

BELGIUM

Marc De Wilde
Clubs de Rire de Belgique asbl /
Lachclubs van België vzw
GSM: 0473/94.21.47
E-mail: marc@clubderire.be
www.clubderire.be

AUSTRALIA

Susan Welch
Brisbane Laughter Clubs
Tel: 0732681036 or 0413651643
Email: welch@powerup.com.au

Shirley Hicks
Sydney Laughter Clubs
Tel: 61 2 98794865
E-mail: greatvibes@amaze.com.au

Phillipa Challis
Melbourne Laughter Clubs
Ph: +61 3 5221 4266
Email: 1challis@tpgi.com.au

GERMANY

**Hamburg Laughter Clubs &
Dr.Kataria's School of Laughter Yoga**
Robert W.L. Butt
Tel: 49 40 2204824
Mobile:0179 1338136
e-mail: rwlb@freenet.de
website: www.lachyoga.de

Wiesbaden

Lachclub Wiesbaden
Tel/Fax: 0611-9749238
E-mail:g.steiner-junker@web.de
www.yogalachen.de

KÖLN

Brigitte Abels
Tel.: 02 21- 91 64 71 28
<brigitte.abels@web.de>
www.hoho-haha.de

Lachclub Köln
Siglinde Kallnbach
Tel:0221-5503261

Lachclub Amorbach
Ralf Drolshagen
Tel. 09373-315463

Lachclub Bad Berleburg
Tel. 02755-968025

Lachclub Bad Honnef
Sieglinde Mack
Tel: 0 22 24-71679

Lachclub Bad Mergentheim
Andreas Brasch
Tel: 0 62 94 - 42 9746

Lachclub Berlin 1
Josefine Grimmer
Tel. 030-8213160

Lachclub Berlin 2
Silvia Schickedanz
Tel:030-85074486
E-mail: streitenundlachen@t-online.de

Lachclub Bonn
Martin Joerdens
Tel:0228-696231

Lachclub Dresden
Volkhard Netz
Tel: 0351-261660

Lachclub Esslingen
Ulrike Kohrs-Gerlach
Tel: 0711-312404

Lachclub Frankfurt
Brigitte Kottwitz
Tel. 069-599726/
E-mail: bkott33333@aol.com
www.saalbau.com/LachClub/index.html

Lachclub Hildesheim
Waltraud Czase
Tel/fax: 05121-63890
E-mail: waltraudczase@gmx.de

Lachclub Kaiserslautern
Heike Degen-Hientz
Tel. 0631-67727

Lachclub Kamp-lintfort
Ruth Lintfort
Tel. 02842-719349

Lachclub Karlsruhe
Georg Schweizer
Tel. 0721-213832

Lachclub Kassel
Claus Enders
Tel. 0561-7390355/

Lachclub Kassel
Reinhard Hoffmann
Tel: 0561-9413012
E-mail: dr.reinhardhoffmann@t-online.de

Lachclub Krefeld
Hartmut Falkenberg
Tel.02151-562611

Lachclub Leipzig
Isolde Schlender
Tel: 0341-3587314

Lachclub Lorrach
Verena Aebischer
Tel: 0041-616412241

Lachclub Oldenburg
Erika Kunkel
Tel: 04481-98165

Lachclub Osnabruck
Birgit Willmann

Tel:05406-3349,
E-mail:lachclub-osnabrueck@freenet.de
http://people.freenet.de/
lachclub-osnabrueck

Lachclub Regensburg
Manfred G. Leitner
T. 0941-5041099/

Lachclub Rendsburg
Hans-Jürgen Ehmke
Tel. 04331-32673

Lachclub Saarland
Manfred lambert
Tel:06851-839583

Lachclub Schildau
Brigitte Tepper
Tel: 034222-40592
E-mail: BrigitteTepper@aol.com
& lachclubsacksen1@aol.com

Lachclub Schriesheim
Florentina Ionescu
Tel. 06203-692258

Lachclub Schwabisch-Hall
Gisela Khodamoradi
Tel: 0791-9597706

Lachclub Stuttgart
Heide Kestin
Tel: 0711-704199
E-mail: hei.kestin@aol.com

Hans-Martin Bauer
Tel:0711-2571258

Lachclub Trier
Jutta Bretz
Tel: 06502-995378

Gauri Shankar Gupta
Tel:06501-4827
E-mail: s.gupta@t-online.de

Lachclub Strassburg
Ute Lorenz,
Tel. 07844-47640
E-mail: Artrium@t-online.de

Lachclub Weibenfels
Sybille Lindeblatt
Tel:03443-803039

Aussenstelee Lachclub
Renate Krohn
Mob:0034-667844170
Tel:0034-952531404

Lachclub Wolfsburg
Waltraud und Siegfried Blach
Tel: 05362-2148,
E-mail:siegfried.blach@wolfsburg.de

DENMARK

Jan Thygesen Poulsen
Tel: (+45) 35384542
e-mail: <jan-thygesen-
poulsen@mail.tele.dk>
www.latterklub.dk

Mariane Eriksen,
Gilleleje afdeling
Telefon 48301391

Inger Pedersen
Herning Zonta Latterklub
Telefon 97129988
e-mail: jpdansk@image.dk

Vibeke Jensen
Kokkedal afdeling
Telefon 49146825

Langenæs afdeling
Martin Østergaard Holm.
Telefon 86 11 72 90

Gunver Harder/
Birte Mathorne
Ry Hjerte Latterklub
Telefon: 86577490

Lydia Davidsen
Sønderborg Afdeling
Telefon: 74 43 62 02

Susanne Willers-Madsen
Uglestrup Afdeling
Telefon 46400912
e-mail: ras-willers@mail.tele.dk

John Christensen
Valby afdeling, Telefon 36 16 83 87

Henrik Sandby Mollerup
Vanløse afdeling
Telefon: 40 14 32 13
e-mail: sandby@sol.dk

Nina Winge Jensen
Vejby afdeling
Telefon: 48 70 61 77
e-mail: ninawinge@yahoo.dk

Kirsten Fich Pedersen
Vesterbro Latterklub
Telefon 33 26 33 60
e-mail: k.fich@sol.dk

Hanne Gottlieb og Ellinor Thomsen
Værlose Latterklub
Telefon 44474734 (Hanne)
Eller 2230 1120 (Ellinor)
e-mail: djeg@post7.tele.dk

Anette Hoffmann
Aalborg afdeling
Telefon: 98124821
e-mail: ettena@forum.dk

Lasse Ljungholm
Århus Latterklub
Telefon 22 63 73 16
e-mail : grevlasse@forum.dk

NORWAY

Franciska Munck
Tel: 0047 - 67919033 &
0047 - 67919282
Mob: 0047-92099455
E-mail: <francisk@online.no>

Annhild Brit Gustavsen
e-mail: anngust@online.no
Tel:+4722836506/+4797780985
www.mamut.com/

ITALY

Milano Laughter Clubs
Roberta Fidora
Tel (house): 0039 02 55602297
Mobile: 0039 335 6852705
e-mail: <rfidora@yahoo.it>

Gubbio Laughter Club
Isis
Tel: 075920271
E-mail: umbria2000@retein.net

Laughter Club in Naples
Ciro Serio
E-mail: ciro.serio@it.ey.com
Tel: Office:++39.081.2480111

Laughter Club of Rome
Laura Toffolo
E-mail: ltoffolo@yahoo.com

Siracusan Laughter Club
Dott. Franco Scirpo
E-mail: frascirp@tin.it
www.laterapiadellarisata.it

SWEDEN

Kalmar Laughter Clubs
Maud Skoog Brandin
Tel: 0480-22480
Mobil: 0709-850385
e-mail: maud@skrattaforlivet.se

Stockholm Laughter Clubs
Lena Ulfsdotter Högnelid
Tel 46-856433934
Mob 0709-508532
E-mail: giraffenskratt@telia.com

Malmo Laughter Club
SKRATTKAMMAREN
E-mail: vivi@skrattkammaren.se
E-mail: ulla@skrattkammaren.se
www.skrattkammaren.se
Tel 070-4940439 Vivi
073-7302749 Ulla

Gothenburg Laughter Club
Agneta Bratt
E-mail: agneta@skratta.nu
www.skratta.nu
Tel: 031-163435 /031-165654

Lund Laughter Clubs
Charlotte Schanner
Tel: 046 505 20
Mob: 073 70 80 705
E-mail: schanner@swipnet.se

UNITED KINGDOM

London Laughter Club
Julie Whitehead
Call 020 7733 2389
e-mail: londonlaughter@aol.com
& NewPlaces2@aol.com
www.laughteryoga.co.uk

Central London Laughter Club,
Justin Hoffman
mail:<justin_hoffman@onetel.net.uk>
Tel: +44 7967 800 217

Bristol Laughter Club
Joe Hoare
mail: speakers4life@yahoo.co.uk
www.bristollaughterclub.com
Tel:07812159943-01179522292

Birmingham Laughter Club
Paul Maguire,
Call 0121 7065715

<paul.maguire@understandyou.com>
www.understandyou.com

SWITZERLAND

Zurich Laughter Clubs
Eva Bischofberger
Tel 01. 261 86 05 also
E-mail: eva.bi@freesurf.ch

Karin Bettina Gisler
Tel.+4113822520/0794203918
e-mail:
<karin.gisler@playback-theater.ch>

HUNGARY

Budapest Laughter Clubs
Mr. Ferenc Domjan
E-mail: rabies@freemail.hu

Tel:36-1-275-3842-
36-30-241-1962
http://www.agykontroll.hu/

AUSTRIA

Laughter Clubs of Austria
Ellen Müller
Tel:+43 69915235001
E-mail: lachyoga@gmx.at
http://www.lachclub.at

Christa Burger
Tel: +43 (0)676 / 77 66 103
E-mail:
<christaburger@lach-yoga.at>
http://www.lach-yoga.at

Gergely Papp (Ildiko)
E-mail: gergely.papp@chello.at

FINLAND

Essi Tolonen
E-mail:
<essi.tolonen@luukku.com>
Tel :+358 -(0)19 - 367 005
Mobile:+358-(0)50-3700 338

ICELAND

Laughter Club of Iceland
Asta Valdimarsdottir
E-mail:
<avaldimarsdottir@hotmail.com>
Tel: -354 8990 223/47 33 40
18 37, 47 41 27 69 49

Valgerdur Snaeland Jonsdottir
E-mail: valsj@ismennt.is
http://www.hlatur.is

IRELAND

Mary Mitchell
E-mail: mitch50@eircom.net
Tel:00353 86 3880044

SPAIN

Geoffrey John Molloy
E-mail: sivimoll@arrakis.es
Tel:**.34.942.83.27.16 -
**.34.942.83.00.20

FRANCE

Daniel Kiefer
Tel: 0389637101
E-mail:
<hohohahaha@clubderire.com>
http://www.clubdurire.com/

**Le Club de Rire de
REICHSTETT**
Gabrielle BURGARD :
Tel: 03.88.96.25.79
Odile Noblat: 03.88.81.02.71
E-mail: odile.noblat@wanadoo.fr

Le Club de Rire du RIED
Pascale Boissaye: 03.88.92.72.86

**Le Club de Rire de
STRASBOURG (1)**
Fabrice VASSE 06 77 98 37 34

Région AQUITAINE
Le Club de Rire du CAP-FERRET
Michelle OGER:
Tel: 06.61.39.08.68 ou
05.56.03.74.87
Mail:michelleoger@wanadoo.fr

Le Club de Rire "Le Grain d' Folie"
Michelle OGER :
Tel: 06.61.39.08.68 ou
05.56.03.74.87
Josiane et André BARREAU :
Tel: 06.88.73.39.10
Mail: info@stagesvoyages.com

**Le Club de Rire de
GRADIGNAN**
Bernadette BRUN:
05.56.89.55.60
Mail:rireabordeaux@wanadoo.fr

Le Club de Rire de PESSAC
Elisabeth: Tel: 06 84 05 98 00
Mail : rirepessac@wanadoo.fr

Région BASSE-NORMANDIE
**Le Club de Rire de
HEROUVILLE**
Jérôme Tchernobaeff
Tel:0231944721-0686102530
Mail:
lutinoetetheatre@netcourrier.com

Région BOURGOGNE
**Le Club de Rire de DIJON
"Le Point**
Martine BUTTARD GERBENNE :
Tel: 03.80.23.84.97 -
06.30.08.29.25
Mail:martine.clown@libertysurf.fr
Jean Marie GERBENNE :
Tel: 03.80.23.84.97 -
06.30.07.47.24
Mail: jm.gerbenne@libertysurf.fr

Région BRETAGNE
Le Club de Rire de LOC MARIA
Sylviane Colombani :
Tel: 02.98.48.52.44

**Le Club de Rire du
MORBIHAN**
Salvatore Augeri: 02.97.47.10.27

Le Club de Rire de BREST
Sylviane Colombani :
Tel: 02.98.48.52.44
Le Club de Rire de LESNEVEN
Sylviane Colombani :
Tel:02.98.48.52.44

Région CENTRE
Le Club de Rire de TOURS
JOSIANE : 06 84 56 92 30

**Le Club de Rire de
BAILLEAU-LE-PIN**
Framboise: Tél. 02 3725 4573
Mail : frambco@club-internet.fr

Région FRANCHE-COMTE
Le Club de Rire de BESANÇON
Jacques OUDOT -
Tél. 03 81 59 97 86

Le Club de Rire de MACON
Joël Viaud - Tél. 03.85.29.96.23

Région ILE-DE-FRANCE
Daniel Lucchina -
Tel: 02.37.48.13.39 ou

06.07.98.52.71
Daniel Lucchina-
06.07.98.52.71
Mail: daniel.lucchina@wanadoo.fr

Le Club de Rire de PARIS 5e
Annick 06.83.21.20.89
Christine 06.09.13.63.88
Mail: rire-et-rire-encore@wanadoo.fr

Le Club de Rire de PARIS 6e
Françoise Rousse
Tel: 06.13.55.71.50 ou
01.43.47.28.22

Le Club de Rire de PARIS 9e
Agnès Le Mahieu
06.81.04.44.38 ou
01.55.06.13.80
Mail:
clubderiredu9e@yahoo.fr

**Le Club de Rire de PARIS
10e**
Ludovic 06-18-05-75-24
Mail:
mmassage@hotmail.com

**Le Club de Rire de PARIS 11e
: "ON oZE Rire"**
Véronique: Tel:
01.43.70.77.39

**Le Club de Rire de PARIS
11e**
Jocelyne Le Moan :
Tel: 06.11.63.60.94
Mail : lemoanj@free.fr
Brigitte Asselineau :
Tel: 06.82.93.14.96
Mail:brigitteasselineau@hotmail.com

**Le Club de Rire de PARIS
12e**
Françoise Rousse
Tel: 06.13.55.71.50 ou
01.43.47.28.22

**Le Club de Rire de PARIS
14e**
Caroline: Tel: 01.40.65.04.23

**Le Club de Rire de
VINCENNES**
Françoise Rousse
Tel: 06.13.55.71.50 ou
01.43.47.28.22

Club de Rire d'ENGHIEN
Isabelle & Stéphanie

Tel: 06.63.56.76.38 ou
06.68.51.36.85
Mail: clubderiredenghien@yahoo.fr

Club de rire de GUYANCOURT
Jocelyne 06.73.05.50.74

Région LANGUEDOC-ROUSSILLON

Le Club de Rire de FRONTIGNAN
Co' Cosseron
Tel: 06.15.31.28.65
Mail : clubderire@frée.fr
http://clubderire.free.fr

Région LORRAINE

Le Club de Rire de NANCY
Marlène Klein -
Tél. 03 83 37 62 91

Région MIDI-PYRENEES

Le Club de Rire de TOULOUSE LE VERNET
Elisabeth Dejean
Tel: 06.19.85.27.33

Région NORD-PAS-DE-CALAIS

Le Club de Rire de LILLE
Tél : 03.20.57.07.48
Mail : clubrirelille@wanadoo.fr

Le club du rire de LAMBERSART
Jacques SION -
Tel: 03.20.92.39.14
Mail : kiks.sion@free.fr

Le Club de Rire de HAUTRAGE (Belgique)
Bernard Cotroux
Tél : (+32) (65) 62 39 05
Mail: bernard.cotroux@skynet.be

RÉGION PICARDIE

Le Club de Rire d'AMIENS
Véronique VILTART :
Tel: 03 22 88 14 73
Mail : clubrireamiens@wanadoo.fr

Région PAYS-DE-LOIRE

Le Club de Rire du MANS
Nathalie Riviere
Tel: 02.47.95.58.85. et
06.84.83.03.13.

Le Club de Rire de la SARTHE
Annie vidie - 02 43 81 00 41.
Mail: annie.vidie@laposte.net

Région POITOU-CHARENTES

Le Club de Rire d'ANGOULEME et du GRAND ANGOULEME
Michel Arnoux 05.45.64.74.35
Mail : miarnoux@wanadoo.fr

Le Club de Rire de NIORT "Gai Rire"
Danièle Baudry -
02.51.51.96.27-06.83.41.46.56

Région PROVENCE-ALPES-COTE D'AZUR

Le Club de Rire d'AIX EN PROVENCE
Guy Monnet 4.42.57.25.72
Mail : monnet.guy@free.fr

Le Club de Rire de TOULON
David et Isabelle Benisty
Tel: 04.94.04.57.97

Le Club de Rire de CAGNES SUR MER
Cannet: 04 93 45 97 15
Maréchal Juin:04 92 13 28 16

Région RHONE-ALPES

Le Club de Rire de CALUIRE
Association, D.C.C- 04.78.08.00.92

Le Club de Rire du Salève à COPPONEX
Bénédicte HAURI -
Tel:04.50.32.04.78-06.24.46.56.91

Le Club de Rire de GEX
Michèle ANDRE -
Tel: 06.73.66.23.98

Le Club de Rire de LYON
Joelle COCHEZ - 06 86 94 90
Mail : clubderiredelyon@free.fr

Le Club de Rire de GRIGNY
Stéphane Cellier - 04 78 51 05
45 / 06 86 03 30 09

Le Club de Rire de OULLINS
Stéphane Cellier - 04 78 51 05
45 / 06 86 03 30 09

Le Club de Rire de ALBENS
Michèle ANDRÉ- 06.73.66.23.98

Le Club de Rire des BAUGES
Michèle ANDRÉ- 06.73.66.23.98

Le Club de Rire de MEYLAN
Viviane - 04 76 41 31 00 ou
06 71 770 442

IRAN

Mr. Majid Pezeshki
E-mail: majidpz@noavar.com
http://www.naslenowandish.com
Tel:0098-21-6952547/8

DUBAI (U.A.E)

Mr. M. Ram
Tel.: 3527803 / 050 4584303
E-mail:<rightsel@emirates.net.ae>

PHILIPPINES

Manish Panchal
Tel:+63-9168-447599
E-mail: mmmip@mail.aim.edu.ph
http://www.laughterclub-ph.batcave.net/

SINGAPORE

Singapore Laughter League

Thomas Peh Chee Kin
Tel:653405171/Mob:97726723
E-mail: Chee_Kin_PEH@pa.gov.sg

Zareena Bana
Tel: 3459014
E-mail: zareen@singnet.com.sg

Gellene Lim (Miss)
Northeast Tampines GRC
Laughter Club
Tel: (65) 7873955
<Gellene_LIM@pa.gov.sg>

MALAYSIA

Mahes Karuppiah
Home Tel 03-22730137,
Office 20933927 or
Mobile 012-3203035
E-mail: healtsen@tm.net.my

(For complete list of Laughter Club in India, visit www.laughteryoga.org)